Sign Up Online

HIGH SCHOOL ELA-1 Practice

Get Digital Access To

2 ELA-1 Practice Tests

5 ELA-1 Domains

Register Now

Url: www.lumoslearning.com/a/tedbooks

Access Code: **ELA1HS-52803-P**

High School ELA 1 Practice Workbook - English Language Arts Online Assessments and Standards-based Lessons: Lumos Skills Mastery Grade 9

Contributing Author	-	**Frances Havard**
Contributing Author	-	**Stephanie Green**
Contributing Author	-	**Tom Farr**
Contributing Author	-	**Dana Ahmuty**
Contributing Author	-	**Amy Flanders**
Executive Producer	-	**Mukunda Krishnaswamy**
Designer and Illustrator	-	**Vaishnavi K R**

ISBN-10: 1949855139

ISBN-13: 978-1949855135

Printed in the United States of America

Last updated - January 2023

For permissions and additional information contact us

Lumos Information Services, LLC

PO Box 1575, Piscataway, NJ 08855-1575

http://www.LumosLearning.com

Email: support@lumoslearning.com

Tel: (732) 384-0146

Fax: (866) 283-6471

Lumos Learning

Step Up Your Skills

Table of Contents

INTRODUCTION

This book is designed to help students get High School ELA 1 rehearsal along with standards aligned with rigorous skills practice. ELA 1 is one of the credits that students will have to earn as a part of English Language Arts credit requirement for High School Graduation.

Unlike a traditional book, this Lumos tedBook offers two full-length practice tests in the online version. Taking these tests will not only help students get a comprehensive review of standards assessed in ELA 1 but also become familiar with technology-enhanced question types.

After students take the test online, educators can use the score report to assign specific lessons provided in this book.

Students will obtain a better understanding of each standard and improve on their weaknesses by practicing the content of this workbook. The lessons contain rigorous questions aligned to the state standards and substandards. Taking the time to work through the activities will enable students to become proficient in each grade level standard.

About Lumos Smart Test Prep Methodology:

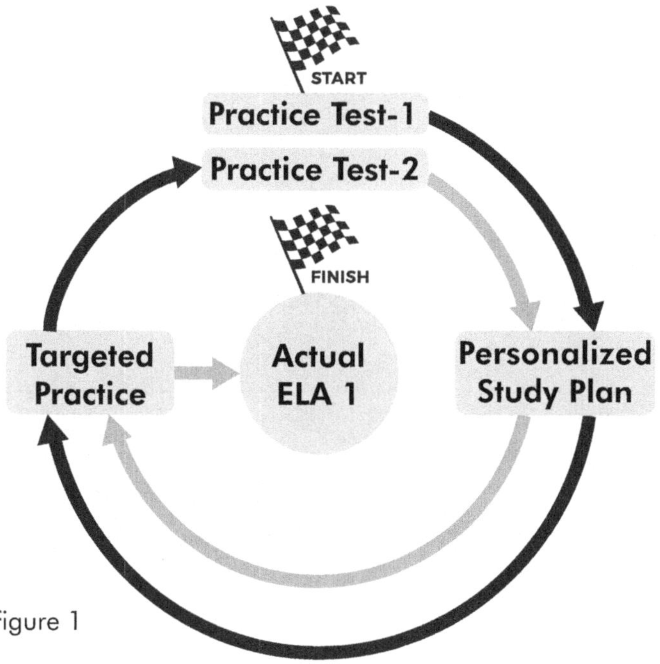

Figure 1

With more than a decade of experience and expertise in developing practice resources for standardized tests, Lumos Learning has developed the most efficient methodology to help students succeed on the state assessments (See Figure 1).

Lumos Smart Test Prep Methodology offers students realistic ELA 1 assessment rehearsal along with providing an efficient pathway to overcome each proficiency gap.

The process starts with students taking the online diagnostic assessment. This online diagnostic test will help assess students' proficiency levels in various standards. With the completion of this diagnostic assessment, Lumos generates a personalized study plan with a standard checklist based on student performance in the online diagnostic test. Parents and educators can use this study plan to remediate the proficiency gaps with targeted standards-based practice available in the workbook.

After student completes the targeted remedial practice, they should attempt the second online ELA 1 practice test. Upon finishing the second assessment, Lumos will generate another individualized study plan by identifying topics that require more practice. Based on these practice suggestions, further skill-building activities can be planned to help students gain comprehensive mastery needed to ensure success on the state assessment.

How will Lumos StepUp® program help students in preparing for the end of course exams of High School ELA credit programs?

The Lumos StepUp® program for High School ELA courses includes

(a) Two Full-length practice tests

(b) Get realistic practice through Online Assessments. It gives students the opportunity to practice test-taking skills, familiarize with the format of the test and efficiently review the key topics. The results will help you get insights into your child's strengths and weaknesses in various content areas. These insights could be used to help your child strengthen their skills in topics where they are having difficulty. This test practice helps them improve speed and accuracy while taking the actual High School ELA 1 Assessments.

(c) StepUp® has great learning content with access to hundreds of activities and Online workbooks.

(d) Your child's work is carefully and meticulously tracked throughout the program. Easy-to-use, advanced and real-time reports will help you identify weak areas and tailor personalized learning plans for your child.

(e) The StepUp® program allows your child to prepare at a pace that is right for him or her. This student-centric approach, combined with instant feedback boosts student confidence and improves learning outcomes.

(f) StepUp® program can be accessed through a number of devices that include, PC, tablet and smart-phones and it is available 24×7. This convenience helps to enable anywhere learning.

Chapter 1

Lumos Smart Test Prep Methodology

Step 1: Access Online ELA1 Practice Test

The online ELA1 practice tests mirror the actual English Language Arts in the number of questions, item types, test duration, test tools, and more.

After completing the test, your student will receive immediate feedback with detailed reports on standards mastery and a personalized study plan to overcome any learning gaps. With this study plan, use the next section of the workbook to practice.

Use the URL and access code provided below or scan the QR code to access the first ELA1 practice test to get started.

URL	QR Code
Visit the URL below and place the book access code **www.lumoslearning.com/a/tedbooks** **Access Code: ELA1HS-52803-P**	

Step 2: Review the Personalized Study Plan Online

After students complete the online Practice Test 1, they can access their individualized study plan from the table of contents (Figure 2) Parents and Teachers can also review the study plan through their Lumos account (parent or teacher) portal.

Lumos StepUp ELA 1 Practice Program

HOMEWORK

Lesson Name		Total Questions	Total Points	Incorrect	Student Score	% Score	Pending
PT1 ELA 1 Practice Test I	Study Plan	4	4	3	I	25%	0
Practice Test 1		4	4	3	I	25%	
Practice Test 2							

BACK COURSE **Lumos Smart Test Practice: Personalized Study Plan for Sam**

Lumos StepUp - Online Practice and Assessments - ELA 1

Upgrade to Full Program

Based on your performance in the online Practice Test 1, we recommend the following additional practice.
Please uses the related lessons in the ELA 1 practice book you purchased.

50 90

EXPORT AS EXCEL

Lesson Name	Standard Info	☐ Targeted practice status	Percentage Score
Reading: Literature			
Grammar and Usage Conventions	L.9-10.1	☐	0%
Capitalization, Punctuation, and Spelling	L.9-10.2	☐	0%
Functions of Language	L.9-10.3	☐	0%

Figure 2

Step 3: Complete Targeted Practice

Using the information provided in the study plan report, complete the targeted practice using the appropriate lessons to overcome proficiency gaps. With lesson names included in the study plan, find the appropriate topics in this workbook and answer the questions provided. Students can refer to the answer key and detailed answers provided for each lesson to gain further understanding of the learning objective. Marking the completed lessons in the study plan after each practice session is recommended.(See Figure 3)

BACK COURSE **Lumos Smart Test Practice: Personalized Study Plan for Sam**

Lumos StepUp - Online Practice and Assessments - ELA 1

Upgrade to Full Program

Based on your performance in the online Practice Test 1, we recommend the following additional practice.
Please uses the related lessons in the ELA 1 practice book you purchased.

50 90

EXPORT AS EXCEL

Lesson Name	Standard Info	☐ Targeted practice status	Percentage Score
Reading: Literature			
Grammar and Usage Conventions	L.9-10.1	■	0%
Capitalization, Punctuation, and Spelling	L.9-10.2	■	0%
Functions of Language	L.9-10.3	☐	0%

Figure 3

Step 4: Access the Practice Test 2 Online

After completing the targeted practice in this workbook, students should attempt the second ELA1 practice test online. Using the student login name and password, login to the Lumos website to complete the second practice test.

Step 5: Repeat Targeted Practice

Repeat the targeted practice as per Step 3 using the second study plan report for Practice test 2 after completion of the second ELA 1 rehearsal.

Visit www.lumoslearning.com/a/lstp for more information on Lumos Smart Test Prep Methodology or Scan the QR Code

What if I buy more than one Lumos Study Program?

Step 1 ⟶ **Visit the URL given below and login to your account**

www.lumoslearning.com

Step 2 ⟶ Click on **'My Subscriptions'** under the **"Account"** tab and goto **"My tedBook"**

Place the Book Access Code and submit.

Step 3 ⟶ **Add the new book**

To add the new book for a registered student, choose the **'Existing Student'** button, select the student and submit.

To add the new book for a new student, choose the **'Add New Student'** button and complete the student registration.

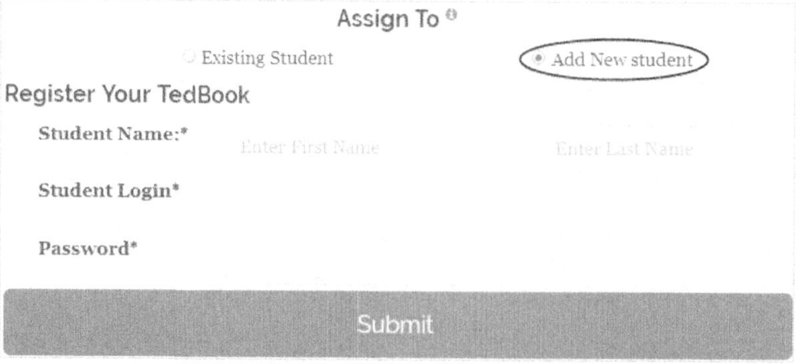

Test Taking Tips

1) **The day before the test,** make sure you get a good night's sleep.

2) On the day of the test, be sure to eat a good hearty breakfast! Also, be sure to arrive at school on time.

3) During the test:

- **Read every question carefully.**
    - Do not spend too much time on any one question. Work steadily through all questions in the section.
    - Attempt all of the questions even if you are not sure of some answers.
    - If you run into a difficult question, eliminate as many choices as you can and then pick the best one from the remaining choices. Intelligent guessing will help you increase your score.
    - Also, mark the question so that if you have extra time, you can return to it after you reach the end of the section.
    - Some questions may refer to a graph, chart, or other kind of picture. Carefully review the infographics before answering the question.
    - Be sure to include explanations for your written responses and show all work.

- **While Answering TECR questions.**
    - Read the directions of each question. Some might ask you to drag something, others to select, and still others to highlight. Follow all instructions of the question (or questions if it is in multiple parts)

Reading: Literature

This Covers standards from RL.9-10.1 to RL.9-10.9

Passage 1: The Open Boat

None of them knew the color of the sky. Their eyes glanced level, and were fastened upon the waves that swept toward them. These waves were of the hue of slate, except for the tops, which were of foaming white, and all of the men knew the colors of the sea. The horizon narrowed and widened and dipped and rose, and at all times its edge was jagged with waves that seemed thrust up in points like rocks.

Many a man ought to have a bathtub larger than the boat which here rode upon the sea. These waves were most wrongfully and barbarously abrupt and tall, and each froth-top was a problem in small boat navigation.

The cook squatted in the bottom and looked with both eyes at the six inches of boat's side which separated him from the ocean. His sleeves were rolled over his fat forearms, and the two flaps of his unbuttoned vest dangled as he bent to bail out the boat. Often he said: "Oh! That was a narrow clip."
As he remarked it, he invariably gazed eastward over the broken sea.
The oiler, steering with one of the two oars in the boat, sometimes raised himself suddenly to keep clear of water that swirled in over the stern. It was a thin little oar, and it seemed often ready to snap.

The correspondent, pulling at the other oar, watched the waves and wondered why he was there.
The injured captain, lying in the bow, was at this time buried in that profound dejection and indifference which comes, temporarily at least, to even the bravest and most enduring. When without warning the firm fails, the army loses, and the ship goes down. The mind of the master of a vessel is rooted deep in the timbers of her. Though he commanded for a day or a decade, this captain had on him the stern impression of a scene in the greys of dawn of seven turned faces. Later a stump of a top-mast with a white ball on it that slashed to and fro at the waves went low and lower and down. Thereafter there was something strange in his voice. Although steady, it was deep with mourning and of a quality beyond oration or tears.

"Keep her a little more south, Billie," said he.
"A little more south,'sir," said the oiler in the stern.

A seat in this boat was not unlike a seat upon a bucking bronco and by the same token, a bronco is not much smaller. The craft pranced and reared and plunged like an animal. As each wave came and she rose for it, she seemed like a horse making at a fence outrageously high. The manner of her scramble over these walls of water is a mystic thing, and moreover at the top of them were ordinarily these problems in white water. The foam racing down from the summit of each wave required a new leap and a leap from the air. Then, after scornfully bumping a crest, she would slide and race and splash down a long incline. It would arrive bobbing and nodding in front of the next menace.

A singular disadvantage of the sea lies in the fact that after successfully surmounting one wave, you discover that there is another behind. It is just as important and just as nervously anxious to do something effective in the way of swamping boats. In a ten-foot dinghy, one can get an idea of the resources of the sea in the line of waves that is not probable to the average experience which is never at sea in a dinghy. As each wall of water approached, it shut all else from the view of the men in the boat. It was not difficult to imagine that this particular wave was the final outburst of the ocean and the last effort of the grim water. There was a terrible grace in the move of the waves, and they came in silence, save for the snarling of the crests.

In the pale light, the faces of the men must have been grey. Their eyes must have glinted in strange ways as they gazed steadily astern. Viewed from a balcony, the whole thing would doubtlessly have been weirdly picturesque. However, the men in the boat had no time to see it. If they had had leisure, there were other things to occupy their minds. The sun swung steadily up the sky, and they knew it was broad day because the color of the sea changed from slate to emerald-green, streaked with amber lights, and the foam was like tumbling snow. The process of the breaking day was unknown to them.They were aware only of this effect upon the color of the waves that rolled toward them.

Excerpt from A Letter from Joseph Conrad

To this writer of the sea, the sea was not an element. It was a stage, where displayed an exhibition of valor and of such achievement as the world had never seen before. The greatness of that achievement cannot be pronounced imaginary since its reality has affected the destinies of nations.

Nevertheless, in its grandeur it has all the remoteness of an ideal.

Note : Only spelling mistakes, if any, in the above passage has been corrected. No other corrections, including grammatical, have been made so that the originality of the passage is maintained.

1. Which of the following quotes from the story best supports the captain's feelings of the situation?

Ⓐ "The injured captain, lying in the bow, was at this time buried in that profound dejection and indifference…"

Ⓑ "Although steady, it was deep with mourning and of a quality beyond oration or tears."

Ⓒ "The mind of the master of a vessel is rooted deep in the timbers of her."

Ⓓ "Keep her a little more south, Billie," said he.

2. **What can you tell about the interaction among the four men who are trying to survive the seas?**

Ⓐ They have united to resolve the problem with the sea.
Ⓑ They have each established their own job to do as they did on the ship.
Ⓒ They seem to be upset with each other in how they are resolving their problem.
Ⓓ The captain is leading his team without receiving any input from them.

3. **How does the four men's survival in the dinghy develop in the story?**

Ⓐ By the captain taking charge and demanding his men comply with each task or suffer the consequences.
Ⓑ By creating a chronological order of events in the plot
Ⓒ By describing how each man worked together to try to make it to shore
Ⓓ By detailing the harsh movement of the waves on the men's dinghy

4. **What impact does imagery in the sentence below have on the passage's tone?**

A seat in this boat was not unlike a seat upon a bucking bronco and by the same token, a bronco is not much smaller. The craft pranced and reared and plunged like an animal.

Ⓐ When the boat began to prance, the author displayed a sensitive tone to this part of the story.
Ⓑ The violent bucking bronco shows a serious tone due to their chaotic situation.
Ⓒ The bronco's movement displays the sympathetic tone toward the men.
Ⓓ With a sarcastic tone, the author uses an analogy of a bucking bronco to describe the men's feelings.

5. **Regarding the men's encounter with surviving the ocean after a shipwreck, what did the pace of the sea's movements and the men's action create?**

Ⓐ Mystery
Ⓑ Tension
Ⓒ Passion
Ⓓ Anger

6. **The author Stephen Crane wrote this story after his encounter as a news reporter on a sinking ship. He and three others tried to survive the open sea after their ship sunk. Through which character in the story can you see Stephen Crane's point of view? Write the Correct Answer in the below box.**

Ⓐ The Captain, because as a writer he is taking command of the story.
Ⓑ The Correspondent, because as a news reporter he represented every man.
Ⓒ The Oiler, because he was the most experienced man on the ship.
Ⓓ The Cook, because he was most likely the most intimidated by the sea.

7. **Which statement most accurately compares the description of the sea in the letter to the sea in Crane's story?**

Ⓐ They both reveal a mystery surrounding the sea that a few discovered.
Ⓑ They both convey the vastness of the sea as an ongoing entity.
Ⓒ They both reveal the beauty of the sea as a visual image.
Ⓓ They both depict the sea as always receiving attention from those near or on the sea.

Name ______________________ Date ______________

Passage 2: Two Thanksgiving Day Gentlemen

Stuffy had always wondered why the Old Gentleman spoke his speech rather sadly. He did not know that it was because he was wishing every time that he had a son to succeed him. A son who would come there after he was gone. It would be a son who would stand proud and strong before some subsequent Stuffy, and say, " In memory of my father." Then it would be an Institution.

But the Old Gentleman had no relatives. He lived in rented rooms in one of the decayed old family brownstone mansions in one of the quiet streets east of the park. In the winter he raised fuchsias in a little conservatory the size of a steamer trunk. In the spring he walked in the Easter parade. In the summer he lived at a farmhouse in the New Jersey hills and sat in a wicker armchair. He would speak of a butterfly, the ornithoptera amphrisius, that he hoped to find some day. In the autumn he fed Stuffy a dinner. These were the Old Gentleman's occupations.

Stuffy Pete looked up at him for a half minute stewing and helpless in his own self-pity. The Old Gentleman's eyes were bright with the giving pleasure. His face was getting more lined each year, but his little black necktie was in as jaunty a bow as ever, and the linen was beautiful and white. His gray mustache was curled carefully at the ends. Then Stuffy made a noise that sounded like peas bubbling in a pot. Speech was intended and as the Old Gentleman had heard the sounds nine times before, he rightly construed them into Stuffy's old formula of acceptance.

"Thank you, sir. I'll go with you, and much obliged. I'm very hungry, sir."

The coma of repletion had not prevented from entering Stuffy's mind the conviction that he was the basis of an Institution. His Thanksgiving appetite was not his own. It belonged by all the sacred rights of established custom. It was not by the actual Statute of Limitations to this kind old gentleman who bad preempted it. True, America is free, but in order to establish tradition someone must be a repetend. In other words, it must be a repeating decimal. The heroes are not all heroes of steel and gold. See one here that wielded only weapons of iron, badly silvered, and tin.

The Old Gentleman led his annual protege southward to the restaurant and to the table where the feast had always occurred. They were recognized.

"Here comes the old guy," said a waiter, "he brings that same bum to a meal every Thanksgiving." The Old Gentleman sat across the table glowing like a smoked pearl at his corner stone of future ancient Tradition. The waiters heaped the table with holiday food. Stuffy, with a sigh that was mistaken for hunger's expression, raised a knife and fork and carved for himself a crown of imperishable bay.

No more valiant hero ever fought his way through the ranks of an enemy. Turkey, chops, soups, vegetables, pies, disappeared before him as fast as they could be served. Gorged nearly to the uttermost when he entered the restaurant, the smell of food had almost caused him to lose his honor as a gentleman. However, he rallied like a true knight. He saw the look of beneficent happiness on the Old Gentleman's face. It was a happier look than even the fuchsias and the ornithoptera amphrisius had ever brought to it. He had not the heart to see it wane.

In an hour Stuffy leaned back with a battle won. "Thank you kindly, sir," he puffed like a leaky steam pipe. "Thank you kindly for a hearty meal." Then he arose heavily with glazed eyes and started toward the kitchen. A waiter turned him about like a top and pointed him toward the door. The Old Gentleman carefully counted out $1.30 in silver change leaving three nickels for the waiter.

They parted as they did each year at the door. The Old Gentleman was going south, and Stuffy went north.
Around the first corner Stuffy turned, and stood for one minute. Then he seemed to puff out his rags as an owl puffs out his feathers and fell to the sidewalk like a sunstricken horse.

When the ambulance came the young surgeon and the driver groaned softly at his weight. Stuffy and his two dinners went to the hospital. There they stretched him on a bed and began to test him for strange diseases with the hope of getting a chance at some problem with the bare steel.

And then an hour later another ambulance brought the Old Gentleman. They laid him on another bed and spoke of appendicitis for he looked good for the bill.

"That nice old gentleman over there, now," he said, "you wouldn't think that was a case of almost starvation. Proud old family, I guess. He told me he hadn't eaten a thing for three days."

Note: Only spelling mistakes, if any, in the above passage has been corrected. No other corrections, including grammatical, have been made so that the originality of the passage is maintained.

1. What quote from the passage lets the reader know that the two men have had Thanksgiving dinner together before?

Ⓐ "No more valiant hero ever fought his way through the ranks of an enemy."
Ⓑ "The Old Gentleman led his annual protege southward to the restaurant and to the table where the feast had always occurred."
Ⓒ "The heroes are not all heroes of steel and gold."
Ⓓ "It was a happier look than even the fuchsias and the ornithoptera amphrisius had ever brought to it."

2. How does the staff at the restaurant react to the two men eating Thanksgiving Dinner?

Ⓐ They feel sorry for them.
Ⓑ They think it is disappointing.
Ⓒ They think it is adorable.
Ⓓ They think it is special.

3. How is the theme of gluttony developed in this passage?

Ⓐ By showing that eating too much can cause problems.
Ⓑ By showing that eating Thanksgiving dinner should be done together like the two characters.
Ⓒ The Old Gentleman and Stuffy continue a tradition despite what others think.
Ⓓ When the two gentlemen eat Thanksgiving dinner together, they realize they are not lonely.

4. What tone is the author conveying in the following sentence from the passage?

Stuffy and his two diners went to the hospital.

Ⓐ Uneasy
Ⓑ Righteous
Ⓒ Humor
Ⓓ Apologetic

5. What is the meaning of the figurative language in the line below?
No more valiant hero ever fought his way through the ranks of an enemy.

Ⓐ The men ate as much as possible.
Ⓑ The men had fought together in a war.
Ⓒ Waiters struggled to bring enough food to the table to satisfy their customers.
Ⓓ The Old Gentlemen had a hard time paying for the entire meal.

6. What element is found in the passage above?

Ⓐ A Parallel plot
Ⓑ A Flashback
Ⓒ A Soliloquy
Ⓓ An Allusion

7. The going of the two men to the hospital, is indicative of what type of literary device?

Ⓐ Dramatic Irony
Ⓑ Sarcasm
Ⓒ Verbal Irony
Ⓓ Situational Irony

Passage 3: The McWilliamses and the Burglar Alarm

The conversation drifted smoothly and pleasantly along from weather to crops, from crops to literature, from literature to scandal, from scandal to religion. Then it took a random jump and landed on the subject of burglar alarms. Now for the first time Mr. McWilliams showed feeling. Whenever I perceive this sign on this man's dial, I comprehend it, lapse into silence and give him opportunity to unload his heart. He said but with ill-controlled emotion.

"I will not give one single cent for a burglar alarm, Mr. Twain—not a single cent—and I will tell you why. When we were finishing our house, we found we had a little cash left over on account of the plumber not knowing it. I was for enlarging the hearth with it because I was always unaccountably down on the hearth somehow. However, Mrs. McWilliams said no, let's have a burglar alarm. I agreed to this compromise. I will explain that whenever I want a thing, and Mrs. McWilliams wants another thing, and we decide upon the thing that Mrs. McWilliams wants—as we always do—she calls that a compromise. The man came up from New York and put in the alarm and charged three hundred and twenty-five dollars for it. He said we could sleep without uneasiness now. So we did for a while—say a month. Then one night we smelled smoke, and I was advised to get up and see what the matter was. I lit a candle and started toward the stairs. I met a burglar coming out of a room with a basket of our tin utensils which he had mistaken for solid silver in the dark. He was smoking a pipe. I said, 'My friend, we do not allow smoking in this room.' He said he was a stranger and could not be expected to know the rules of the house. I said he had been in many houses just as good as this one, and it had never been objected to before. He added that as far as his experience went, such rules had never been considered to apply to burglars, anyway.

"I said, 'Smoke along, then if it is the custom. However, waiving all that, what business have you to be entering this house in this furtive and clandestine way, without ringing the burglar alarm?'

"He looked confused and ashamed and said with embarrassment, 'I beg a thousand pardons. I did not know you had a burglar alarm else I would have rung it. I beg you will not mention it where my parents may hear of it, for they are old and feeble. Such a seemingly cruel breach of the holy conventionalities of our Christian civilization might all too rudely separate the frail bridge. May I trouble you for a match?'

"I said, 'Your sentiments do you honor, but if you will allow me to say it, the metaphor is not your best hold. To return to business, how did you get in here?'

"'Through a second-story window.'

"It was even so. I redeemed the utensils at the pawnbroker's rates, less cost of advertising, bade the burglar goodnight, closed the window after him, and retired to headquarters to report. Next morning, we sent for the burglar-alarm man, and he came up and explained that the reason the alarm did not 'go off' was that no part of the house but the first floor was attached to the alarm. This was simply idiotic because one might as well have no armor on at all in battle as to have it only on his legs. The expert now put the whole second story on the alarm, charged three hundred dollars for it, and went his way. By and by, one night, I found a burglar in the third story about to start down a ladder with a lot of miscellaneous property. My first impulse was to crack his head with a billiard cue, but my second was to refrain from this attention because he was between me and the cue rack. The second impulse was plainly the soundest, so I refrained and proceeded to compromise. I redeemed the property at former rates, after deducting ten percent for use of the ladder. It was my ladder. The next day we sent down for the expert once more and had the third story attached to the alarm for three hundred dollars.

"By this time the burglar alarm had grown to difficult dimensions. It had forty-seven tags on it, marked with the names of the various rooms and chimneys, and it occupied the space of an ordinary wardrobe. The gong was the size of a wash-bowl and was placed above the head of our bed. There was a wire from the house to the coachman's quarters in the stable and a noble gong alongside his pillow.

After spending years of trying to make sure their house is secure, Mr.McWilliams would receive a bill like the one below from an expert itemizing the materials used in securing the house.

Wire $2.15
Nipple........................... .75
Two hours' labor 1.50
Wax.............................. .47
Tape............................. .34
Screws........................... .15
Recharging battery .... .98
Three hours' labor 2.25
String........................... .02
Lard .... .66
Pond's Extract 1.25
Springs at 50.................... 2.00
Railroad fares................... 7.25

Note

Only spelling mistakes, if any, in the above passage has been corrected. No other corrections, including grammatical, have been made so that the originality of the passage is maintained.

Name ______________________ Date ______________

1. Find the evidence from the passage that supports the following idea:

Mr. McWilliams really doesn't want a burglar alarm because it's too expensive.

2. How does the interaction between the narrator and the burglar contribute to the theme that burglar alarms are not valuable?

Name ______________________ Date ______________

3. Match the character from the story to how they are portrayed in the passage.

	calm and relaxed	greedy	closed-minded	fearful
Mr. McWilliams	○	○	○	○
Mrs. McWilliams	○	○	○	○
Burglar	○	○	○	○
Burlgar Alarm man	○	○	○	○

4. What does the following line mean?

a lot of miscellaneous property

Ⓐ the owners' most expensive jewelery
Ⓑ variety of belongings from the house
Ⓒ large pieces like furniture
Ⓓ different coins

5. What information from the passage foreshadows that the McWilliams will experience a second burglar?

6. Which phrase below reveals that the passage was during a different time or place?

Ⓐ not a single cent
Ⓑ billiard cue
Ⓒ burglar alarm
Ⓓ coachman's quarters

Name ______________________ Date ______________

7. The narrator's point of view concerning the effectiveness of the burglar alarm can be described as

8. What is the list of items that Mr. McWilliams had to pay for included in the passage?

9. What is the reason for including the list of items that Mr. McWilliams had to pay an expert to fix?

Ⓐ To allow the reader to sympathize with all the expenses the McWilliamses are being charged
Ⓑ To show how a burglar alarm takes a lot of parts to make it work
Ⓒ To display how difficult it is to make a house burglar-proof
Ⓓ To emphasize how technical a burglar alarm is

Passage 4: How an Old Man Lost his Wen

Many, many years ago there lived a good old man who had a wen like a tennis-ball growing out of his right cheek. This lump was a great disfigurement to the old man, and it so annoyed him that for many years he spent all his time and money in trying to get rid of it. He tried everything he could think of. He consulted many doctors far and near and took all kinds of medicines both internally and externally. It was all of no use. The lump only grew bigger and bigger till it was nearly as big as his face, and in despair he gave up all hopes of ever losing it. He resigned himself to the thought of having to carry the lump on his face all his life.

One day the firewood gave out in his kitchen, so as his wife wanted some at once, the old man took his ax and set out for the woods up among the hills not very far from his home. It was a fine day in the early autumn, and the old man enjoyed the fresh air and was in no hurry to get home. So, the whole afternoon passed quickly while he was chopping wood, and he had collected a goodly pile to take back to his wife. When the day began to draw to a close, he turned his face homewards.

The old man had not gone far on his way down the mountain pass when the sky clouded and rain began to fall heavily. He looked about for some shelter, but there was not even a charcoal-burner's hut near. At last he noticed a large hole in the hollow trunk of a tree. The hole was near the ground, so he crept in easily and sat down in hopes that he had only been overtaken by a mountain shower and that the weather would soon clear.

Much to the old man's disappointment, instead of clearing the rain fell more and more heavily. Finally, a heavy thunder-storm broke over the mountain. The thunder roared so terrifically, and the heavens seemed to be so ablaze with light-ning, that the old man could hardly believe himself to be alive. He thought that he must die of fright. At last, however, the sky cleared, and the whole country was aglow in the rays of the setting sun. The old man's spirits revived when he looked out at the beautiful twilight. He was about to step out from his strange hiding place in the hollow tree when the sound of what seemed like the approaching steps of several people caught his ear. He at once thought that his friends had come to look for him. He was delighted at the idea of having some jolly companions with whom to walk home. On looking out from the tree, what was his amazement to see, not his friends, but hundreds of demons coming towards the spot. The more he looked, the greater was his astonishment. Some of these demons were as large as giants. Others had great big eyes out of all proportion to the rest of their bodies. Others again had absurdly long noses, and some had such big mouths that they seemed to open from ear to ear. All had horns growing on their foreheads. The old man was so surprised at what he saw that he lost his balance and fell out of the hollow tree.Fortunately for him the demons did not see him, as the tree was in the background. So, he picked himself up and crept back into the tree.

While he was sitting there and wondering impatiently when he would be able to get home, he heard the sounds of happy music, and then some of the demons began to sing.

"What are these creatures doing?"said the old man to himself. "I will look out, it sounds very amusing."
On peeping out, the old man saw that the demon chief himself was actually sitting with his back against the tree in which he had taken refuge, and all the other demons were sitting around, some drinking and some dancing. Food and wine were spread before them on the ground, and the demons were evidently having great entertainment and enjoying themselves immensely.

It made the old man laugh to see their strange antics.

"How amusing this is!" laughed the old man to himself "I am now quite old, but I have never seen anything so strange in all my life."

He was so interested and excited in watching all that the demons were doing, that he forgot himself and stepped out of the tree and stood looking on.

Note

Only spelling mistakes, if any, in the above passage has been corrected. No other corrections, including grammatical, have been made so that the originality of the passage is maintained.

1. Write the line from the text that best supports the following idea:

The old man didn't expect the demons to be there.

2. Write the quote from the ones stated below, that best supports the following idea:

The old man was discouraged with the lump on his face and would take more action to get it removed.

Ⓐ "He consulted many doctors far and near"
Ⓑ "there lived a good old man who had a wen like a tennis-ball growing out of his right cheek"
Ⓒ "This lump was a great disfigurement to the old man"
Ⓓ "He resigned himself to the thought of having to carry the lump on his face all his life."

3. Describe how the old man interacts with the demons near the end of the story.

Name ______________________________ Date _______________

As the demons are having fun drinking wine and eating food, the man in the tree is acting _______ __________________________ while looking at the demons.

4. Complete the above sentence.

5. How do the demons at the end of the passage support the central idea of the man's problem?

6. What is the meaning of the word "wen"?

- Ⓐ an upset man
- Ⓑ a painful injury
- Ⓒ dancing demons
- Ⓓ A lump on the skin

7. Which type of literary device is seen in this passage?

- Ⓐ An Allusion
- Ⓑ A Flashback
- Ⓒ A Parallel plot
- Ⓓ A Situational irony

Name ______________________ Date ____________

8. What is the old man's view of the demons?

Name ______________________ Date ______________

Passage 5: Havells Stories from the Odyssey

Directions: Read the rewritten excerpt from H.L . Havell's "Stories from the Odyssey" and Homer's "Odyssey." Then answer the questions.

Thence they came to the land of the Cyclopes, a rude and monstrous tribe but favored of the immortal gods by whose bounty they live. They toil not, neither do they sow, nor till the ground, but the earth of herself brings forth for them a bountiful living of wheat and barley, and huge swelling clusters of the grape. Naught know they of law or civil life, but each lives in his cave on the wild mountainside, dwelling apart, careless of his neighbors with his wife and children.

It was a dark, cloudy night, and a thick mist overspread the sea when suddenly Odysseus heard the booming of breakers on a rocky shore. Before an order could be given, or any measure taken for the safety of the ships, the little fleet was caught by a strong landward current and whirled recklessly through a narrow passage between the cliffs into a land-locked harbor. Drawing their breath with relief at their wonderful escape, they beached their vessels on the level sand and lay down to wait for the day.

In the morning they found that they had been driven to the landward shore of a long island which formed a natural breakwater to a spacious bay with a narrow entrance at either end. The island was thickly covered with woods giving shelter to a multitude of wild goats, its only inhabitants. For the Cyclopes have no ships, so that the goats were left in undisturbed possession, though the place was well suited for human habitation with a deep, rich soil and plentiful springs of water.

The first care of Odysseus was to supply the crews of his vessels, which were twelve in number, with fresh meat. Armed with bows and spears, he and a picked body of men scoured the woods in search of game. They soon obtained a plentiful booty, and nine goats were assigned to each vessel with ten for that of Odysseus. So, all that day till the setting of the sun they sat and feasted on fat venison and drank of the wine which they had taken in their raid on the Thracians.

Early the next morning Odysseus manned his own galley and set forth to explore the mainland leaving the rest of the crews to await his return on the island. As they drew near the opposite shore of the bay, the mariners came in view of a gigantic cavern overshadowed by laurel-trees. Round the front of the cavern was a wide courtyard rudely fenced with huge blocks of stone and unhewn trunks of trees.

Homer's "Odyssey"

"The land of Cyclops first, a savage kind,
Nor tamed by manners, nor by laws confined:
Untaught to plant, to turn the glebe, and sow,
They all their products to free nature owe:
The soil, untill'd, a ready harvest yields,
With wheat and barley wave the golden fields;
Spontaneous wines from weighty clusters pour,
And Jove descends in each prolific shower,
By these no statues and no rights are known,
No council held, no monarch fills the throne;
But high on hills, or airy cliffs, they dwell,
Or deep in caves whose entrance leads to hell.
Each rules his race, his neighbour not his care,
Heedless of others, to his own severe.

Note

Only spelling mistakes, if any, in the above passage has been corrected. No other corrections, including grammatical, have been made so that the originality of the passage is maintained.

1. Explain how you know that Odysseus is concerned about the well-being of his crew. Use evidence to support your explanation.

2. How is the theme that Odysseus is starting to encounter trouble developed?

Ⓐ By showing the inhabitant's horrific appearance.
Ⓑ By explaining how the people who inhabit the land are barbaric.
Ⓒ By describing that these people grow their own food.
Ⓓ By showing that little information is known about these people because they don't associate with others.

3. Even though each version of the story provides different details, which idea do they both include?

Ⓐ Odysseus's thoughts about the Cyclops
Ⓑ the Cyclops's economy
Ⓒ the layout of the land
Ⓓ the anger of the Cyclops

Name ______________________________ Date ________________

4. **How does the structure affect the length of Havell's version of the Odyssey when compared to the original?**

5. **Match the following details from each selection to the version where they are found.**

	Havell's version	Homer's original version
_____Created a sense of fear when Odysseus arrived	◯	◯
Portrays the Cyclops as a destructive force	◯	◯
Described the lack of government where the Cyclops lived	◯	◯

6. **What difference is found in Homer's version showing that the Cyclops were productive with their agriculture? Write the correct answer in the box below.**

Ⓐ A few different pieces of equipment are used in the agricultural process.
Ⓑ The Cyclops had big feasts and prepared the foods for these feasts.
Ⓒ Wine was made from the clusters of grapes grown.
Ⓓ Cyclops grew a variety of crops on their land.

Name ______________________________ Date ______________

7. In the passage, Cyclops did not interact with those around them.

What details from the original version support this claim?

8. In regards to the text structure, describe the freedom Havell has in writing compared to Shakespeare.

Name ______________________ Date ______________

Passage 6: Eleanor

I have come to see a race of people noted for vigor of fancy and ardor of passion. Men have called me mad, but the question is not yet settled whether madness is or is not the loftiest intelligence. They who dream by day are cognizant of many things which escape those who dream only by night. In their gray visions they obtain glimpses of eternity, and thrill, in awakening to find that they have been upon the verge of the great secret. They learn something of the wisdom which is of good and more of the mere knowledge which is of evil. They penetrate, however, rudderless or compassless into the vast ocean of the overwhelming light and again like the adventures of the Nubian geographer.

We will say, then, that I am mad. I grant, at least, that there are two distinct conditions of my mental existence. It is the condition of a lucid reason not to be disputed and belonging to the memory of events forming the first era of my life—and a condition of shadow and doubt, relating to the present and to the recollection of what constitutes the second great era of my being. Therefore, what I shall tell of the earlier period to what I may relate of the later time, give only such credit as may seem due or doubt it altogether.

She whom I loved in youth, and of whom I now pen calmly and distinctly these remembrances was the sole daughter of the only sister of my mother long departed. Eleonora was the name of my cousin. We had always dwelled together beneath a tropical sun in the Valley of the Many-Colored Grass. No unguided footstep ever came upon that valley, for it lay away up among a range of giant hills that hung beetling around it. It was shutting out the sunlight from its sweetest recesses. No path was flattened in its vicinity and to reach our happy home, there was need of putting back with force the foliage of many thousands of forest trees, and of crushing to death the glories of many millions of fragrant flowers. Thus, it was that we lived all alone knowing nothing of the world without the valley—I, and my cousin, and her mother.

From the dim regions beyond the mountains at the upper end of our encircled domain, there crept out a narrow and deep river, brighter than all save the eyes of Eleonor. It would be winding stealthily about in courses, it passed away at length through a shadowy gorge among hills still dimmer than those whence it had issued. We called it the "River of Silence," for there seemed to be a hushing influence in its flow. No murmur arose from its bed and so gently it wandered along that the pearly pebbles upon which we loved to gaze far down within its bosom stirred not at all but lay in a motionless content each in its own old station shining on gloriously forever.

The margin of the river and of the many dazzling streams that glided through devious ways into its channel as well as the spaces that extended from the margins away down into the depths of the streams until they reached the bed of pebbles at the bottom. These spots, not less than the whole surface of the valley from the river to the mountains that pulled it in were carpeted all by a soft green grass, thick, short, perfectly even, and vanilla-perfumed, but so besprinkled throughout with the yellow buttercup, the white daisy, the purple violet, and the ruby-red asphodel, that its exceeding beauty spoke to our hearts in loud tones.

Note :

Only spelling mistakes, if any, in the above passage has been corrected. No other corrections, including grammatical, have been made so that the originality of the passage is maintained.

Name ________________________________ Date ________________

1. What evidence below shows that the narrator had a troubling childhood?

Ⓐ "It is the condition of a lucid reason not to be disputed and belonging to the memory of events forming the first era of my life and a condition of shadow and doubt,"
Ⓑ "She whom I loved in youth, and of whom I now pen calmly and distinctly these remembrances"
Ⓒ "Therefore, what I shall tell of the earlier period to what I may relate of the later time, give only such credit as may seem due or doubt it altogether."
Ⓓ "It was shutting out the sunlight from its sweetest recesses."

2. What is Eleanor's part in the passage?

3. What word best describes the narrator's love for Eleanor?

Ⓐ discreet
Ⓑ tenderly
Ⓒ obsessive
Ⓓ smitten

4. In what way is the passage structured to the reader?

Ⓐ By including background information before explaining the narrator's love for Eleanor.
Ⓑ Using a cause and effect structure that lets the reader know how the narrator came to love Eleanor.
Ⓒ To provide the setting about where the narrator met Eleanor.
Ⓓ By explaining the main characters and where they live.

5. Match the words with their meanings.

	to jut out	government land	strong emotion
"ardor of passion"	◯	◯	◯
"hung beetling around it"	◯	◯	◯
"encircled domain"	◯	◯	◯

6. The narrator compares men who are in love with a woman to a vast ocean because ________

7. What word below is considered a word used during earlier times and in England?

Ⓐ youth
Ⓑ mad
Ⓒ streams
Ⓓ doubt

8. Why does the author's view of Eleanor include nature-centric scenes and items?

Passage 7: Little Women

Mrs. Chester's fair was so very elegant and select that it was considered a great honor by the young ladies of the neighborhood to be invited to take a table, and everyone was much interested in the matter. Amy was asked, but Jo was not which was fortunate for all parties as her elbows were decidedly akimbo at this period of her life. It took a good many hard knocks to teach her how to get on easily. The 'haughty, uninteresting creature' was let severely alone, but Amy's talent and taste were duly complimented by the offer of the art table, and she exerted herself to prepare and secure appropriate and valuable contributions to it.

Everything went on smoothly till the day before the fair opened. Then there occurred one of the little skirmishes which it is almost impossible to avoid when some five-and-twenty women, old and young, with all their private piques and prejudices, try to work together.

May Chester was rather jealous of Amy because the latter was a greater favorite than herself, and just at this time several trifling circumstances occurred to increase the feeling. Amy's dainty pen-and-ink work entirely eclipsed May's painted vases—that was one thorn. Then the all-conquering Tudor had danced four times with Amy at a late party and only once with May—that was thorn number two. But the chief grievance that rankled in her soul and gave an excuse for her unfriendly conduct, was a rumor which some obliging gossip had whispered to her that the March girls had made fun of her at the Lambs' house. All the blame of this should have fallen upon Jo, for her naughty imitation had been too lifelike to escape detection, and the frolicsome Lambs had permitted the joke to escape. No hint of this had reached the culprits, however, and Amy's dismay can be imagined when the very evening before the fair, as she was putting the last touches to her pretty table, Mrs. Chester who of course, resented the supposed ridicule of her daughter, said, in a bland tone, but with a cold look...

"I find, dear, that there is some feeling among the young ladies about my giving this table to anyone but my girls. As this is the most prominent, and some say the most attractive table of all, and they are the chief getters-up of the fair. It is thought best for them to take this place. I'm sorry, but I know you are too sincerely interested in the cause to mind a little personal disappointment, and you shall have another table if you like."

Mrs. Chester fancied beforehand that it would be easy to deliver this little speech, but when the time came, she found it rather difficult to utter it naturally with Amy's unsuspicious eyes looking straight at her full of surprise and trouble.

Amy felt that there was something behind this but could not guess what and said quietly, feeling hurt and showing that she did, "Perhaps you had rather I took no table at all?"

"Now, my dear, don't have any ill-feeling, I beg. It's merely a matter of expediency. You see, my girls will naturally take the lead, and this table is considered their proper place. I think it very appropriate to you, and feel very grateful for your efforts to make it so pretty, but we must give up our private wishes, of course. I will see that you have a good place elsewhere.Wouldn't you like the flower table? The little girls undertook it, but they are discouraged. You could make a charming thing of it, and the flower table is always attractive you know."

"Especially to gentlemen, "added May, with a look which enlightened Amy as to one cause of her sudden fall from favor. She colored angrily, but took no other notice of that girlish sarcasm, and answered with unexpected amiability...

"It shall be as you please, Mrs. Chester. I'll give up my place here at once, and attend to the flowers, if you like."

Note

Only spelling mistakes, if any, in the above passage has been corrected. No other corrections, including grammatical, have been made so that the originality of the passage is maintained.

Name ______________________ Date ______________

1. Find the evidence from the passage that shows a time when someone was purposefully overlooked.

2. At the end of the passage, Amy and Mrs. Chester have an interaction about the table. How would you describe this interaction?

Ⓐ comical
Ⓑ excited
Ⓒ serious
Ⓓ angry

3. Why was it unusual for Mrs. Chester to ask Amy to go to another table?

Name ______________________ Date ______________

4. **Complete the table below, matching the characters with the lesson they learned.**

	Mrs. Chester	May Chester	Amy
Refrain from making comments about people	○	○	○
Jealousy is a poor quality	○	○	○
Do not get involved in your daughter's problems.	○	○	○

5. **Why did the author use the term "five-and-twenty" to describe the amount of women at a party?**

6. **Explain the meaning of the following phrase.**

"Merely a matter of expediency."

Name ______________________________ Date ________________

7. **How can this passage's structure best be described?**

Ⓐ It's descriptive
Ⓑ It's problem/solution
Ⓒ It's flashback
Ⓓ It's spatial

8. **How is the author's view of Amy positive?**

Name ______________________ Date ______________

Passage 8: Muriels Bright Idea

Directions: Read the rewritten excerpt from "Muriel's Bright Idea." Then answer the questions.

My friend Muriel is the youngest daughter in a large family of busy people. They are in moderate circumstances, and the original breadwinner has been long gone. So, in order to enjoy many of the comforts and a few of the luxuries of life the young people have to be wage- earners. I am not sure that they would enjoy life any better than they do now if such were not the case, though there are doubtless times when they would like to be less busy. Still, even this condition has its compensations.

"Other people do not know how lovely vacations are," was the way Esther expressed it as she sat one day on the side porch, hands folded lightly in her lap, and an air of delicious idleness about her entire person. It was her week of absolute leisure which she had earned by a season of hard work. She is a public-school teacher belonging to a section and grade where they work their teachers fourteen hours of the twenty-four.

Alice is a music-teacher and goes all day from house to house in town and from school to school with her music-roll in hand. Ben, a young brother, is studying medicine in a doctor's office also in town and serving the doctor between times to pay for his opportunities. There are two others, an older brother who just started in business for himself and a sister in a training- school for nurses.

So it was that this large family scattered each morning to their duties in the city ten miles away and gathered at night like chickens to the home nest which was mothered by the dearest little woman who gave much of her time and strength to the preparation of favorite dishes with which to greet the wage-earners as they gathered at night around the home table. It is a very happy family, but it was not about any of them that I set out to tell you. In truth, it was Muriel's apron that I wanted to talk about, but it seemed necessary to describe the family in order to secure full appreciation of the apron.

Muriel, I should tell you, is still a high-school girl, hoping to be graduated next year, though at times a little anxious lest she may not pass and with ambitions to enter college as soon as possible.

The entire family has ambitions for Muriel, and I believe that she will get to college in another year. About her apron, I saw it first one morning when I crossed the street to my neighbor's side door that opens directly into the large living room and met Muriel in the doorway, as pretty a picture as a fair-haired, bright-eyed girl of seventeen can make. She was in what she called her uniform, a short dress made of dark print, cut lower in the neck than a street dress. It had elbow sleeves and a bit of white braid stitched on their bands and around the square neck set off the little costume charmingly.

Her apron was of strong dark-green denim wide enough to cover her dress completely. It had a bib waist held in place by shoulder straps, and the garment fastened behind with a single button making it adjustable in a second. Its distinctive feature was a row of pockets—or rather several rows of them—extending across the front breadth. They were of varying sizes, and all bulged out as if well filled.

"What in the world?" I began, and stared at the pockets. Muriel's merry laugh rang out.

"Haven't you seen my pockets before?" she asked. "They astonish you, of course.

Name ______________________________ Date ______________

Everybody laughs at them, but I am proud of them. They are my own invention. You see, we are such a busy family all day long and so tired when we get home at night, that we have a bad habit of dropping things just where they happen to land and leaving them. By the last of the week this big living room is a sight to behold. It used to take half my morning to pick up the thousand and one things that did not belong here and carry them to their places. You do not know how many journeys I had to make because I was always overlooking something. So, I invented this apron with a pocket in it for every member of the family, and it works like a charm.

Note :

Only spelling mistakes, if any, in the above passage has been corrected. No other corrections, including grammatical, have been made so that the originality of the passage is maintained.

1. What is the first clue that made the reader realize that the apron looked different from the others?

Ⓐ "Her apron was of strong dark-green denim wide enough to cover her dress completely."
Ⓑ "It had a bib waist held in place by shoulder straps,"
Ⓒ "What in the world?" I began, and stared at the pockets.
Ⓓ "Its distinctive feature was a row of pockets—or rather several rows of them—extending across the front breadth."

2. State the evidence from the passage that shows that Muriel comes from a single parent family.

Name ______________________________ Date ________________

3. **Why is the apron important to the story's theme?**

4. **Match the character with their description to the central idea.**

	Muriel's older siblings	Muriel	Narrator
sentimental about the apron	◯	◯	◯
outsider from the family	◯	◯	◯
workers who contribute to the family	◯	◯	◯

5. **What is the central idea of the passage?**

Ⓐ It's about a girl who is ready to graduate from high school.
Ⓑ It's about the youngest girl in a family and how she contributes by working.
Ⓒ It's about all of the pockets that are sewn into an apron.
Ⓓ It's about how a young girl is treated by her older siblings.

6. **How does the narrator feel about Muriel and her family?**

Ⓐ impressed
Ⓑ confused
Ⓒ envious
Ⓓ cheerful

7. Why is the passage so structured as to have the description of the family first?

8. How is pacing used in the passage?

Name ______________________ Date ______________

Passage 9: John and Mary Lambs Version

There was a law in the city of Athens which gave its citizens the power of compelling their daughters to marry whomsoever they pleased. For upon a daughter's refusal to marry the man her father had chosen to be her husband, the father was empowered by this law to cause her to be put to death. This is because fathers do not often desire the death of their own daughters even though they do happen to prove a little refractory. This law was seldom or never put in execution. Perhaps the young ladies of that city were not infrequently threatened by their parents with the terrors of it.

There was one instance, however, of an old man, whose name was Egeus, who actually did come before Theseus (at that time the reigning duke of Athens), to complain that his daughter Hermia, whom he had commanded to marry Demetrius, a young man of a noble Athenian family, refused to obey him because she loved another young Athenian named Lysander. Egeus demanded justice of Theseus and desired that this cruel law might be put in force against his daughter.

Hermia pleaded in excuse for her disobedience that Demetrius had formerly professed love for her dear friend Helena. Helena loved Demetrius to distraction, but this honorable reason which Hermia gave for not obeying her father's command moved not the stern Egeus.

William Shakespeare's Version

EGEUS. Happy be Theseus, our renowned Duke!
THESEUS. Thanks, good Egeus; what's the news with thee?
EGEUS. Full of vexation come I, with complaint
Against my child, my daughter Hermia.
Stand forth, Demetrius. My noble lord,
This man hath my consent to marry her.
Stand forth, Lysander. And, my gracious Duke,
This man hath bewitch'd the bosom of my child.
Thou, thou, Lysander, thou hast given her rhymes,
And interchang'd love-tokens with my child;
Thou hast by moonlight at her window sung,
With feigning voice, verses of feigning love,
And stol'n the impression of her fantasy
With bracelets of thy hair, rings, gawds, conceits,
Knacks, trifles, nosegays, sweetmeats- messengers
Of strong prevailment in unhardened youth;
With cunning hast thou filch'd my daughter's heart;
Turn'd her obedience, which is due to me,
To stubborn harshness. And, my gracious Duke,
Be it so she will not here before your Grace
Consent to marry with Demetrius,
I beg the ancient privilege of Athens:
As she is mine I may dispose of her;
Which shall be either to this gentleman

Or to her death, according to our law
Immediately provided in that case.
THESEUS. What say you, Hermia? Be advis'd, fair maid.
To you your father should be as a god;
One that compos'd your beauties; yea, and one
To whom you are but as a form in wax,
By him imprinted, and within his power
To leave the figure, or disfigure it.
Demetrius is a worthy gentleman.
HERMIA. So is Lysander.
THESEUS. In himself he is;
But, in this kind, wanting your father's voice,
The other must be held the worthier.
HERMIA. I would my father look'd but with my eyes.
THESEUS. Rather your eyes must with his judgment look.
HERMIA. I do entreat your Grace to pardon me.
I know not by what power I am made bold,
Nor how it may concern my modesty
In such a presence here to plead my thoughts;
But I beseech your Grace that I may know
The worst that may befall me in this case,
If I refuse to wed Demetrius.
THESEUS. Either to die the death, or to abjure
For ever the society of men.
Therefore, fair Hermia, question your desires,

Note

Only spelling mistakes, if any, in the above passage has been corrected. No other corrections, including grammatical, have been made so that the originality of the passage is maintained.

1. Based on the passage, what emotion did Hermia most likely develop towards her father?

Ⓐ Impatience
Ⓑ Envy
Ⓒ Fear
Ⓓ Bitterness

2. Which phrase best shows the formal tone of Shakespeare's version?

Ⓐ Immediately provided
Ⓑ beseech your Grace
Ⓒ what's the news
Ⓓ Thanks, good

3. What does the structure of Shakespeare's version include?

Ⓐ Dialogue and characters
Ⓑ Parallel plots
Ⓒ Flashback
Ⓓ Irony

4. Which cultural problem is shown in both excerpts of "A Midsummer Night's Dream"?

Ⓐ Child abuse
Ⓑ Immigration rights
Ⓒ Court procedures
Ⓓ Women's rights

5. What is emphasized in Shakespeare's version compared to the Lambs' version?

Ⓐ The father's reasoning for bringing his daughter to court
Ⓑ The daughter's explanation of why she does not want to marry Demetrius
Ⓒ The background of Demetrius
Ⓓ The background of the law for punishing disobedient daughters

6. Read the lines below from Shakespeare's version and John and Mary Lamb's version. In Shakespeare's version, the father, Egeus, is referred to as a god, but how is the father described in John and Mary Lamb's version?

Shakespeare:

What say you, Hermia? Be advis'd, fair maid.
To you your father should be as a god;

John and Mary Lamb:

but this honorable reason which Hermia gave for not obeying her father's command moved not the stern Egeus.

Ⓐ The same way as in Shakespeare's version
Ⓑ As a concerned father
Ⓒ As the complete opposite
Ⓓ With compassion towards his daughter

7. How did the Lambs relay the information about the law for punishing their daughters when they refuse to marry the person of their father's choice?

Ⓐ By using a similar format as Shakespeare
Ⓑ By providing it as background information
Ⓒ By considering it to be part of a student's prior knowledge
Ⓓ As part of the plot

Name ______________________________ Date ______________

Passage 10: Sweetser's Ten Boys from Dickens

Directions: Read the rewritten excerpt from Kate Dickinson Sweetser's "Ten Boys from Dickens" and Charles Dickens' "A Christmas Carol." Then answer the questions.

Charles Dickens has given us no picture of Tiny Tim, but at the thought of him comes a vision of a delicate figure less boy than spirit. We seem to see a face oval in shape and fair in coloring. We see eyes deep-set and grey shaded by lashes as dark as the hair parted from the middle of his low forehead. We see a sunny, patient smile which from time to time lights up his whole face, and a mouth whose firm, strong lines reveal clearly the beauty of character and the happiness of disposition which were Tiny Tim's.

He was a rare little chap indeed and a prime favorite as well. Ask the Crachits old and young whose smile they most desired, whose applause they most coveted, whose errands they almost fought with one another to run, whose sadness or pain could most affect the family happiness, and with one voice they would answer, "Tim's!"

It was Christmas Day, and in all the suburbs of London there was to be no merrier celebration than at the Crachits. To be sure, Bob Crachit had but fifteen "Bob" himself a week on which to clothe and feed all the little Crachits, but what they lacked in luxuries they made up in affection and contentment and would not have changed places, one of them, with any king or queen.

Dickens' A Christmas Carol

So Martha hid herself and in came little Bob, the father, with at least three feet of comforter exclusive of the fringe hanging down before him. His threadbare clothes darned up and brushed to look seasonable. Tiny Tim is upon his shoulder. Alas for Tiny Tim, he bore a little crutch and had his limbs supported by an iron frame!

"Why, where's our Martha?" cried Bob Cratchit, looking round.
"Not coming," said Mrs. Cratchit.
"Not coming!" said Bob with a sudden declension in his high spirit, for he had been Tim's blood horse all the way from church, and had come home rampant. "Not coming upon Christmas day!"

Martha didn't like to see him disappointed. If it were only in joke, she would understand. So, she came out prematurely from behind the closet door and ran into his arms while the two young Cratchits hustled Tiny Tim and bore him off into the washhouse that he might hear the pudding singing in the copper.

"And how did little Tim behave?" asked Mrs. Cratchit when she had rallied Bob on his credulity, and Bob had hugged his daughter to his heart's content.

"As good as gold," said Bob, "and better. Somehow, he gets thoughtful sitting by himself so much and thinks the strangest things you ever heard. He told me coming home that he hoped the people saw him in the church because he was a cripple, and it might be pleasant to them to remember upon Christmas day who made lame beggars walk and blind men see."

Bob's voice was tremulous when he told them this and trembled more when he said that Tiny Tim was growing strong and hearty.

Note :

Only spelling mistakes, if any, in the above passage has been corrected. No other corrections, including grammatical, have been made so that the originality of the passage is maintained.

Name ______________________________ Date ________________

1. **What word from "A Christmas Carol" best shows that this story took place in England?**

Ⓐ beggars
Ⓑ copper
Ⓒ pudding
Ⓓ washhouse

2. **How is Sweetser's version different?**

3. **Match the way the Cratchits are described in each version.**

	Sweetser's version	Dickens' version	Both
a loving family	○	○	○
Tiny Tim as happy	○	○	○
that Tiny Tim might be mischievous	○	○	○
Tiny Tim as disabled	○	○	○

4. **The Dickens' version uses ________________________________ to show the feelings and actions of the characters unlike Sweetser's version.**

Name ______________________________ Date ______________

5. The original version of the story uses more ______________________________ than Sweetser's by stating "been Tim's blood horse," "heard the pudding singing in the copper," and "as good as gold."

6. Why did Sweetser most likely choose base Tiny Tim's description on the original passage?

7. Unlike, Sweetser's version, the Dickens' version uses ______________________________ to show the feelings and actions of the characters.

Name ______________________________ Date ________________

8. What criticism does Sweetser give about Dickens' version of "A Christmas Carol?"

Ⓐ that the Crachits were poor
Ⓑ that one of the main characters was not appropriately described
Ⓒ that it was merely implied that the next day was Christmas
Ⓓ that Scrooge was a miserable man at the beginning of the story

9. In what way does Sweetser's version show how poor the Cratchits were based on Bob's salary compared to Dickens' version?

Reading: Informational Text

This Covers standards from RI.9-10.1 to RI.9-10.7

Passage 1: My Life and Work

Directions: Read the rewritten passage of Henry Ford's "My Life and Work" answer the following questions.

I believe that this was the first moving line ever installed. The idea came in a general way from the overhead trolley that the Chicago packers use in packaging beef. We had previously assembled the fly-wheel magneto in the usual method. With one workman doing a complete job, he could turn out from thirty-five to forty pieces in a nine-hour day or about twenty minutes to an assembly. What he did alone was then spread into twenty-nine operations that cut down the assembly time to thirteen minutes, ten seconds. Then we raised the height of the line eight inches which was in 1914 and cut the time to seven minutes. Further experimenting with the speed that the work should move quickly and cut the time down to five minutes. In short, the result is the aid of scientific study one man is now able to do somewhat more than four did only comparatively few years ago. That line established the efficiency of the method, and we now use it everywhere. The assembling of the motor, formerly done by one man, is now divided into eighty-four operations. Those men do the work that three times their number formerly did. In a short time, we tried out the plan on the framework on the car or the chassis.

About the best we had done in stationary chassis assembling was an average of twelve hours and twenty-eight minutes per chassis. We tried the experiment of drawing the chassis with a rope and windlass down a line two hundred fifty feet long. Six assemblers traveled with the chassis and picked up the parts from piles placed along the line. This rough experiment reduced the time to five hours fifty minutes per chassis. In the early part of 1914 we elevated the assembly line. We had adopted the policy of "man-high" work. We had one line twenty-six and three-quarter inches and another twenty-four and one-half inches from the floor to suit squads of different heights. The waist-high arrangement and a further subdivision of work so that each man had fewer movements cut down the labor time per chassis to one hour thirty-three minutes. Only the chassis was then assembled in the line. The body was placed on "John R. Street" which is the famous street that runs through our Highland Park factories. Now the line assembles the whole car.

It must not be imagined, however, that all this worked out as quickly as it sounds. The speed of the moving work had to be carefully tried out. In the fly-wheel magneto we first had a speed of sixty inches per minute. That was too fast. Then we tried eighteen inches per minute. That was too slow. Finally, we settled on forty-four inches per minute. The idea is that a man must not be hurried in his work. He must have every second necessary but not a single unnecessary second. We have worked out speeds for each assembly, for the success of the chassis assembly caused us gradually to overhaul our entire method of manufacturing and to put all assembling in mechanically driven lines. The chassis assembling line, for instance, goes at a pace of six feet per minute; the front axle assembly line goes at one hundred eighty-nine inches per minute. In the chassis assembling are forty-five separate operations or stations. The first men fasten four mud-guard brackets to the chassis frame. Then the motor arrives on the tenth operation and so on in detail. Some men do only one or two small operations whereas others do more. The man who places a part does not fasten it because the part may not be fully in place until after several operations later. The man who puts in a bolt does not put on the nut. The man who puts on the nut does not tighten it. On operation number thirty-four, the budding motor gets its gasoline. It has previously received lubrication. On operation number forty-four, the radiator is filled with water, and on operation number forty-five the car drives out onto John R. Street.

Note

Only spelling mistakes, if any, in the above passage has been corrected. No other corrections, including grammatical, have been made so that the originality of the passage is maintained.

Name ______________________________ Date ________________

1. Which evidence from the passage supports the fact that the assembly line was created based on another form of an assembly line method?

Ⓐ "We had previously assembled the fly-wheel magneto in the usual method."
Ⓑ "The idea came in a general way from the overhead trolley that the Chicago packers use in packaging beef."
Ⓒ "I believe that this was the first moving line ever installed."
Ⓓ "Further experimenting with the speed that the work should move quickly and cut the time down to five minutes."

2. Which evidence shows that the assembly line has become popular with companies?

Ⓐ "About the best we had done in stationary chassis assembling was an average of twelve hours and twenty-eight minutes per chassis."
Ⓑ "Those men do the work that three times their number formerly did. In a short time, we tried out the plan on the framework on the car or the chassis."
Ⓒ "The assembling of the motor, formerly done by one man, is now divided into eighty-four operations."
Ⓓ "That line established the efficiency of the method, and we now use it everywhere."

3. Which of the following contributes to the development of the central idea?

Ⓐ the length of time it takes a car to be built using an assembly line
Ⓑ the definition of chassis
Ⓒ when the height of the line was raised
Ⓓ the street where the car was placed

4. What does the author do to reveal information about his assembly line?

5. What is meant by the statement that they "had adopted the policy of 'man-high' work"?

6. Match the vocabulary term from the article to its description.

	a device for raising or lowering something	**electric generator**	**the framework on the car**
fly-wheel magneto	○	○	○
chassis	○	○	○
windlass	○	○	○

7. What is the author's purpose for showing how long each part of the assembly line takes?

Ⓐ to allow the reader to visualize each step in the assembly line
Ⓑ for the method to be replicated
Ⓒ to show in detail how his assembly line worked
Ⓓ to provide details for assembling a car

8. Why does the author describe how the men on the line do not complete the process before sending that part of the car down the assembly line?

Name ______________________ Date ______________

Passage 2: How to Make a Bow and Arrow

Directions: Read the excerpt of "How to Make a Bow and Arrow" from Edward Sylvester Ellis's "Outdoor Life and Indian Stories" and the drawing of the bow and arrow. Then answer the questions.

In the early days the Indian did not have the modern hunting rifle and was compelled to use bow and arrow in the chase. It is well for the modern boy to understand this weapon, for it can be made with ease and much good fun can be had with it. The Indian bow was short because though less efficient it was easier to carry than a long one, yet it did not lack power. We hear that many times Indians shot so hard that their arrows appeared on the far side of the animal, but the long bow, such as was used by the old English archers or bowmen, was much more powerful.

To make the bow take a perfectly sound, straight, well-seasoned stick of about your own height and mark off a space as wide as your hand in the middle for a handle. This space should be left round and about an inch thick. The balance of the stick should be shaved down flat on one side for the front and rounded on the other for the back until it is about one inch wide and three-fourths of an inch thick near the handle tapering to about half that at the ends which are then notched for the cord. Next put on the cord and bend it until it is about five inches from the bow at the center. If one end bends more than the other shave the other end until it becomes even.

After it is trimmed down to your strength finish it with sand-paper. The best woods to use are apple, black walnut, slippery elm, mountain ash or hickory.

More difficult to make than the bow is the arrow. The Indians made arrows of reeds and of straight shoots of arrow-wood or of elder, but we make better arrows out of hickory or ash. The arrow should be twenty-five inches long, round, and three-eighths of an inch thick. It should be notched at one end to take the bow-string, and just below this notch it should have three feathers set around at equal intervals. These feathers are best made from either turkey or goose wings. With a sharp knife cut a strip of the midrib on which is the vein; make three pieces, each two to three inches long. The Indians used to leave the midrib projecting at each end, and by these lash the feathers to the arrow without gluing, but it is easier to glue them and the arrows fly better. Indian arrow-heads were made of sharp flints or pieces of stone lashed to the arrowheads, but the best way to make them now is like the ferrule of an umbrella as this keeps the shaft from splitting. After this the arrow should be painted, both to keep it from warping and to make it easier to find in the forest by its bright color.

After the bow and arrows are made, one must learn to shoot with them. It is well to begin with the target close at hand, and gradually increase the distance as the archer becomes more expert. The Indians generally used their bows at short range so that it was easy to hit the mark, and considered rapid firing more important. In their competitions the prize was given to him who should have the most arrows in the air at once, and it has been said that their record was eight.

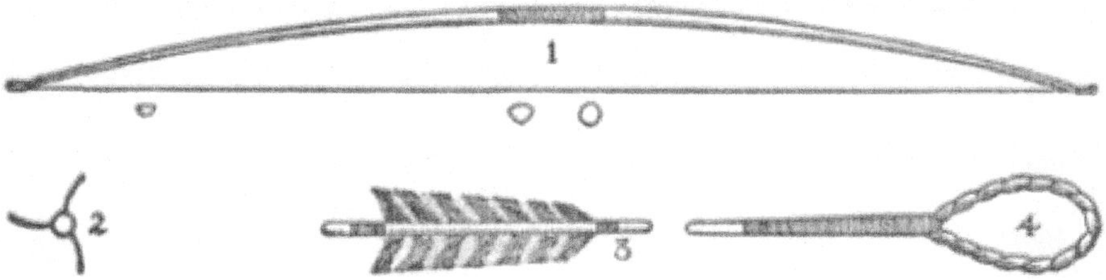

Note :

Only spelling mistakes, if any, in the above passage has been corrected. No other corrections, including grammatical, have been made so that the originality of the passage is maintained.

Name ________________________ Date ______________

1. **Match the evidence with the information it supports. Shows the strength of the Indian's bow and arrow compared to that of others?**

	"The strength of the Indian's bow and arrow is shown compared to that of others."	"Supplies are specific for optimum results."	"Techniques are described to keep the arrows strong."
After this the arrow should be painted, both to keep it from warping and to make it easier to find in the forest by its bright color.	○	○	○
We hear that many times Indians shot so hard that their arrows appeared on the far side of the animal.	○	○	○
These feathers are best made from either turkey or goose wings.	○	○	○

2. **Which choice best explains how the author describes the process of making a bow and arrow?**

Ⓐ By including the materials needed and the process of how to make that part of the bow and arrow
Ⓑ By explaining all of the materials first and then the process
Ⓒ By describing each part of the bow and arrow before explaining the process for making the bow and arrow
Ⓓ By explaining why each part of the bow and arrow helps make this the most powerful bow and arrow

Name ______________________ Date ______________

3. How are the bow and arrow introduced in this passage?

4. What is the meaning of a midrib as it is used in the sentence below?

With a sharp knife cut a strip of the midrib on which is the vein

Ⓐ the elastic on the bow
Ⓑ the notch in the bow
Ⓒ the hair of the feather
Ⓓ the stem of the feather

5. The ferrule is found on the ______________________ of an object.

6. In what way are the author's ideas developed?

Ⓐ By explaining the materials that the Indians used.
Ⓑ By systematically detailing the steps of making and shooting an arrow from a bow.
Ⓒ By describing the difference between making the bow and making the arrow.
Ⓓ By detailing the importance of why the Indians used such a powerful bow and arrow.

Name ______________________ Date ______________

7. Why does the author include the drawing of the arrow, bow, and its parts?

8. Why is there a shaded part in the drawing for the bow (1)?

Name ____________________ Date ____________

Passage 3: How It Works

Directions: Read the excerpt from Archibald Williams's "How It Works" and analyze the drawing. Then answer the questions.

By attaching a small wheel to the end of a Morse-sounder lever, by arranging an ink-well for the wheel to dip into when the end falls, and by moving a paper ribbon slowly along for the wheel to press against when it rises, a self-recording Morse inker is produced. The ribbon-feeding apparatus is set in motion automatically by the current and continues to pull the ribbon along until the message is completed.

The Hughes type-printer covers a sheet of paper with printed characters in bold Roman type. The transmitter has a keyboard on which are marked letters, signs, and numbers. Also, a type-wheel, with the characters on its circumference, rotated by electricity. The receiver contains mechanisms for rotating another type-wheel synchronously—that is, in time—with the first, for shifting the wheel across the paper, for pressing the paper against the wheel and for moving the paper when a fresh line is needed. These are too complicated to be described here in detail. By means of relays one transmitter may be made to work five hundred receivers. In London a single operator controlling a keyboard in the central dispatching office causes typewritten messages to spell themselves out simultaneously in machines distributed all over the metropolis.

The tape machine resembles that is just described in many details. The main difference is that it prints on a continuous ribbon instead of on sheets.

Automatic electric printers of some kind or others are to be found in the foyers of all the principal hotels and clubs of our large cities and in the offices of bankers, stockbrokers, and newspaper editors. In London alone over 500 million words are printed by the receivers in a year.

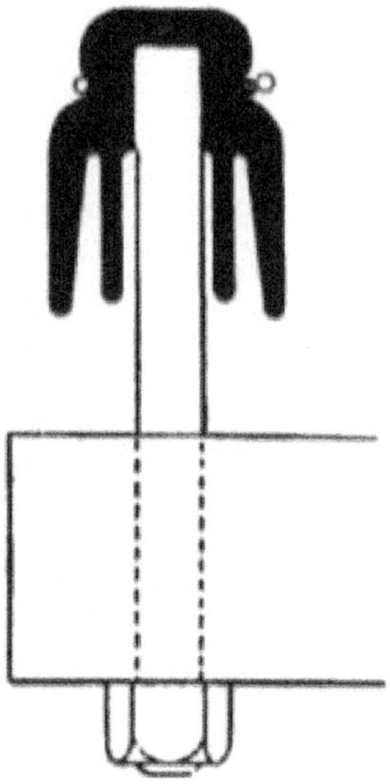

Fig. 58 -- Section of a telegraph wire insulator on its arm. The shaded circle is the line wire, the two blank circles indicate the wire which ties the line wire to the insulator.

Note

Only spelling mistakes, if any, in the above passage has been corrected. No other corrections, including grammatical, have been made so that the originality of the passage is maintained.

Name ______________________________ Date ________________

1. **What evidence reveals that the receiver serves a large number of functions?**

Ⓐ "The tape machine resembles that just described in many details."
Ⓑ "These are too complicated to be described here in detail."
Ⓒ "By means of relays one transmitter may be made to work five hundred receivers."
Ⓓ "The receiver contains mechanisms for rotating another type-wheel synchronously."

2. **The central idea emerges through the description of the telegraph's________________.**

3. **The idea that is established by the author in the first paragraph is that with __________ ____________________________ a telegraph will function properly.**

4. **What purpose does including the drawing with the passage serve?**

Name ______________________________ Date ________________

5. What does the word "metropolis" mean in the sentence below?

In London a single operator controlling a keyboard in the central dispatching office causes typewritten messages to spell themselves out simultaneously in machines distributed all over the metropolis.

Ⓐ Office
Ⓑ City
Ⓒ Telegraph
Ⓓ Desk

6. How is the author's claim about the importance of the wireless telegraph developed?

7. Observe the drawing at the end of the passage.

What does the drawing reveal about the wireless telegraph?

Name ______________________ Date ______________

8. **Match where the information can be found.**

	Drawing	Passage
the position of the wires in relation to the rest of the device	○	○
part of the device functions by electricity	○	○
as the message is received, it types it automatically	○	○

Passage 4: Whales, Dolphins, and Porpoises of the Western North Atlantic

Directions: Read the excerpt from Stephen Leatherwood's, David Caldwell's and Howard Winn's "Whales, Dolphins, and Porpoises of the Western North Atlantic." Then answer the questions.

All five species of large whales with a dorsal fin belong to the same major baleen whale group, the balaenopterid whales or rorquals. All are characterized by the presence of a series of ventral grooves usually visible on stranded specimens and the length and number of which are diagnostic to species. In addition, all species, with the exception of the humpback whale, have at least one distinctive (though often not prominent) ridge along the head from just in front of the blowhole to near the tip of the snout. (The humpback whale, on the other hand, is distinguished by numerous knobs, some of which are located along the line of the head ridge with others scattered on the top of the head.) In Bryde's whale, the single head ridge characteristic of the other rorquals is supplemented by two auxiliary ridges one on each side of the main ridge.

At sea, these whales often appear very similar and must be examined carefully before they can be reliably identified.

In general, though the characteristics of behavior may vary from one encounter to the next, based on the activities in which the animal is engaged, whales in this group may be distinguished from each other on the basis of differences in 1) the size, shape, and position of the dorsal fin and the timing of its appearance on the surface relative to the animal's blow (in general, the larger the whale, the smaller the dorsal fin—the further back its position and the later its appearance on the surface after the animal's blow); 2) the height of body in the area of the dorsal fin, relative to the size of the dorsal fin, which is exposed as the animal sounds; 3) sometimes the blow rate and movement patterns; and 4) the shape and color of the head.

Despite variability in behavior by members of the same species from one encounter to the next, an observer can greatly increase the reliability of his identification by forming the habit of working systematically through a set of characteristics for the species rather than depending on any single characteristic.

There are three species of large whales without a dorsal fin in the western North Atlantic Ocean. Two of these, the bowhead or Greenland whale, and its more widely distributed close relative the right whale, are baleen whales. The third, the sperm whale, is a toothed whale. The first two have relatively smooth backs without even a trace of a dorsal fin. The sperm whale has a humplike low, thick, dorsal ridge, which from certain views particularly when the animal is humping up to begin a dive may be clearly visible and look like a fin. But because the profile of that hump and the knuckles which follow it are often not very prominent in this species, it has been classified with the finless big whales.

All three species are characterized by very distinctive blows or spouts. In both the bowhead and the right whales, the projection of the blow upward from two widely separated blowholes assumes a very wide V-shape with two distinct columns, which may be seen when the animals are viewed from front or back. Though this character may be visible under ideal conditions in many of the other baleen whales species as well, it is exaggerated and uniformly distinct in the bowhead and right whales and may be used as one of the primary key characters. In the sperm whale, the blow emanates from a blowhole which is displaced to the left of the head near the front and projects obliquely forward to the animal's left. This blow seen under ideal conditions positively labels a large whale as a sperm whale.

Note

Only spelling mistakes, if any, in the above passage has been corrected. No other corrections, including grammatical, have been made so that the originality of the passage is maintained.

Name ______________________________ Date ______________

1. **What sentence from the passage supports that the sperm whale is different from the other whales?**

Ⓐ "The third, the sperm whale, is a toothed whale.."
Ⓑ "There are three species of large whales without a dorsal fin in the western North Atlantic Ocean.."
Ⓒ "All three species are characterized by very distinctive blows or spouts.."
Ⓓ "But because the profile of that hump and the knuckles which follow it are often not very prominent in this species, it has been classified with the finless big whales.."

2. **What evidence suggests that all whales look alike?**

Ⓐ "This blow seen under ideal conditions positively labels a large whale as a sperm whale."
Ⓑ "Despite variability in behavior by members of the same species from one encounter to the next,"
Ⓒ "At sea, these whales often appear very similar and must be examined carefully before they can be reliably identified."
Ⓓ "(The humpback whale, on the other hand, is distinguished by numerous knobs, some of which are located along the line of the head ridge with others scattered on the top of the head.)"

3. **Which part of a whale's body shows the difference between other species of whale?**

Ⓐ teeth
Ⓑ mouth
Ⓒ hump
Ⓓ dorsal fin

4. **Match the whale with its description.**

	bumps on its head	**has three ridges on its head**	**has a hump on its back with no dorsal fin**
humpback	○	○	○
sperm	○	○	○
Bryde's whale	○	○	○

Name ______________________________ Date ________________

5. **How does the author reveal the meaning of the word "rorquals"?**

6. **What does "auxiliary" mean in the sentence below?**

In Bryde's whale, the single head ridge characteristic of the other rorquals is supplemented by two auxiliary ridges one on each side of the main ridge.

Ⓐ gray
Ⓑ supportive
Ⓒ backwards
Ⓓ flavorful

7. **What claim does the author indirectly make about different whales?**

Name ______________________________ Date ______________

8. What is the author's purpose in writing this piece about whales? Explain using evidence from the text.

Passage 5: John F. Kennedys Inaugural Address

Vice President Johnson, Mr. Speaker, Mr. Chief Justice, President Eisenhower, Vice President Nixon, President Truman, reverend clergy, fellow citizens, we observe today not a victory of party, but a celebration of freedom—symbolizing an end, as well as a beginning—signifying renewal, as well as change. For I have sworn before you and Almighty God the same solemn oath our forebears prescribed nearly a century and three quarters ago.

The world is very different now. For man holds in his mortal hands the power to abolish all forms of human poverty and all forms of human life. And yet the same revolutionary beliefs for which our forebears fought are still at issue around the globe—the belief that the rights of man come not from the generosity of the state, but from the hand of God.

We dare not forget today that we are the heirs of that first revolution. Let the word go forth from this time and place, to friend and foe alike, that the torch has been passed to a new generation of Americans—born in this century, tempered by war, disciplined by a hard and bitter peace, proud of our ancient heritage—and unwilling to witness or permit the slow undoing of those human rights to which this Nation has always been committed, and to which we are committed today at home and around the world.

Let every nation know, whether it wishes us well or ill, that we shall pay any price, bear any burden, meet any hardship, support any friend, oppose any foe, in order to assure the survival and the success of liberty.

This much we pledge—and more.

To those old allies whose cultural and spiritual origins we share, we pledge the loyalty of faithful friends. United, there is little we cannot do in a host of cooperative ventures. Divided, there is little we can do—for we dare not meet a powerful challenge at odds and split asunder.

To those new States whom we welcome to the ranks of the free, we pledge our word that one form of colonial control shall not have passed away merely to be replaced by a far more iron tyranny. We shall not always expect to find them supporting our view. But we shall always hope to find them strongly supporting their own freedom—and to remember that, in the past, those who foolishly sought power by riding the back of the tiger ended up inside.

To those people in the huts and villages across the globe struggling to break the bonds of mass misery, we pledge our best efforts to help them help themselves, for whatever period is required—not because the Communists may be doing it, not because we seek their votes, but because it is right. If a free society cannot help the many who are poor, it cannot save the few who are rich.

To our sister republics south of our border, we offer a special pledge—to convert our good words into good deeds—in a new alliance for progress—to assist free men and free governments in casting off the chains of poverty. But this peaceful revolution of hope cannot become the prey of hostile powers. Let all our neighbors know that we shall join with them to oppose aggression or subversion anywhere in the Americas. And let every other power know that this Hemisphere intends to remain the master of its own house.

Note

Only spelling mistakes, if any, in the above passage has been corrected. No other corrections, including grammatical, have been made so that the originality of the passage is maintained.

Name ________________________________ Date ________________

1. Find the evidence that shows President Kennedy is referring to Alaska and Hawaii.

2. What evidence in the text supports President Kennedy's decision to keep some laws and add others?

3. What topic does President Kennedy first discuss in his speech?

4. Who is President Kennedy referring to when he says "forebears"?

Ⓐ citizens of the United States
Ⓑ Leaders from other countries
Ⓒ previous presidents
Ⓓ later presidents

Name ________________________ Date ______________

Passage 6: Textiles and Clothing

Directions: Read the excerpt from Kate Heintz Watson's "Textiles and Clothing." Then answer the questions.

Spinning and weaving are among the earliest arts. In the twisting of fibers, hairs, grasses, and sinews by rolling them between the thumb and fingers, palms of the hands, or palms and naked thigh, we have the original of the spinning wheel and the steam-driven cotton spindle. In the roughest plaiting we have the first hint of the finest woven cloth. The need of securing things or otherwise strengthening them then led to binding, fastening, and sewing. The wattle-work hut with its roof of interlaced boughs, the skins sewn by fine needles with entrails or sinews, the matted twigs, grasses, and rushes are all the crude beginnings of an art which tells of the settled life of today.

Nothing is definitely known of the origin of these arts. All is conjecture. They doubtless had their beginning long before mention is made of them in history, but these crafts—spinning and weaving—modified and complicated by inventions and in modern times transferred largely from man to machine were distinctively woman's employment.

The very primitive type of spinning where no spindle was used was to fasten the strands of goats' hair or wool to a stone which was twirled round until the yarn was sufficiently twisted when it was wound upon the stone and the process repeated over and over.

The next method of twisting yarn was with the spindle, a straight stick eight to twelve inches long on which the thread was wound after twisting. At first it had a cleft or split in the top in which the thread was fixed. Later a hook of bone was added to the upper end. The spindle is yet used by the North American Indians, the Italians, and in the Orient. The bunch of wool or flax fibers is held in the left hand. With the right hand the fibers are drawn out several inches and the end fastened securely in the slit or hook on the top of the spindle. A whirling motion is given to the spindle on the thigh or any convenient part of the body. The spindle is then dropped, twisting the yarn, which is wound on the upper part of the spindle. Another bunch of fibers is drawn out, the spindle is given another twirl, the yarn is wound on the spindle, and so on.

A spindle containing a quantity of yarn was found to rotate more easily, steadily and continue longer than an empty one, hence the next improvement was the addition of a whorl at the bottom of the spindle. These whorls are discs of wood, stone, clay, or metal which keep the spindle steady and promote its rotation. The process in effect is precisely the same as the spinning done by our grandmothers, only the spinning wheel did the twisting and reduced the time required for the operation.

Situation: After completing most of the research project about the differences between igneous and sedimentary rocks, part of the requirements of the assignment is to publish the project online for the entire class to see. It is up to each student to find a safe place to publish the project. Below are the requirements of the project.

Project Requirements: Research and create a project that includes a report of at least three typed pages with citation and a visual aid (graph, chart, table, etc.). The topic must cover something that we studied in class this year. You must publish your project for all of the students in our class to see and comment on it.

Note

Only spelling mistakes, if any, in the above passage has been corrected. No other corrections, including grammatical, have been made so that the originality of the passage is maintained.

Name ______________________________ Date ________________

1. **What is the author's purpose for writing this passage? Write the correct answer in the below box.**

Ⓐ To describe how spinning and weaving is now a dying art
Ⓑ To make light of how spinning and weaving can be funny
Ⓒ To explain why people should learn how to spin and weave
Ⓓ To inform the reader about how to spin and weave

2. **What evidence from the passage best shows a gender bias regarding spinning and weaving?**

3. **How is the central idea shaped in the article?**

Ⓐ By providing examples of prominent ways of spinning and weaving.
Ⓑ By describing the ways in which spinning and weaving came to be and how to do it.
Ⓒ By explaining the different types of people who did spinning and weaving.
Ⓓ By detailing the different supplies and equipment that were used in factories.

4. **The author introduces spinning and weaving to the reader by generally describing________________.**

5. **What are sinews as they are described in the sentence from the passage? Write the correct answer in the below box.**

In the twisting of fibers, hairs, grasses, and sinews by rolling them between the thumb and fingers, palms of the hands, or palms and naked thigh, we have the original of the spinning wheel and the steam-driven cotton spindle.

Ⓐ weaving
Ⓑ needles
Ⓒ threads
Ⓓ tendons

6. **How does the passage flow into the description of the types of spinning and weaving?**

7. **"The spindle is yet used by the North American Indians, the Italians, and in the Orient." What purpose does this line serve in the passage? Why do you think the author included it?**

Name ______________________ Date ______________

Passage 7: Common Sense

Directions: Read the rewritten passage Thomas Paine's "Common Sense" and answer the questions

Some writers have so been annoyed by society with the government as to leave little or no distinction between them whereas they are not only different but have different origins. Society is produced by our wants and the government by our wickedness. The former promotes our happiness positively by uniting our affections and the latter negatively by restraining our vices. The one encourages communication and the other creates differences. The first is a supporter, and the last is a punisher.

Society in every state is a blessing, but government even at its best state is but a necessary evil. In its worst state it is an intolerable one. For when we suffer or are exposed to the same miseries by a government, our misfortune is heightened by reflecting that we furnish the means by which we suffer.
Government is the badge of lost innocence, and the palaces of kings are built on the ruins of the places of paradise. If the impulses of a clear conscience, clear expectations, and irresistibly obeyed officials are there, then man would need no other lawgiver. However, that is not the case because he finds it necessary to surrender up a part of his property to furnish means for the protection of the rest. This, he is induced to do by the same cautiousness which in every other case advises him out of two evils to choose the least. Wherefore, security should be the true policy from the government, so that it follows whatever form appears most likely to ensure it to us with the least expense and greatest benefit is preferable to all others.

In order to gain a clear and just idea of the design of the government, let us suppose a small number of people settled in some sequestered part of the earth, unconnected with the rest, they will then represent the first peopling of any country or of the world. In this state of natural liberty, society will be their first thought. A thousand reasons will excite them thereto, the strength of one man is so unequal to his wants, and his mind so unfitted for continuous isolation, that he is soon obliged to seek assistance and relief of another. He requires the same. Four or five united people would be able to raise a tolerable dwelling in the midst of a wilderness, but one man might work out of the common period of life without accomplishing anything. When he had chopped for his timber, he could not remove it, nor build with it after it was removed. Therefore, hunger in the meantime would bother him from his work, and every different need calls him in a different way. Disease would disable him from living and reduce him to a state in which he might rather be said to perish than to die.

Thus, necessity would soon form our newly arrived emigrants into society the common blessings of the obligations of law and government unnecessary while they remained perfectly fair to each other. They prevail the first difficulties of emigration which bound them together in a common cause. They will begin to relax in their duty and attachment to each other. This is careless of establishing some form of government to supply the defect of moral virtue.

Some convenient tree will afford them a State-House, under the branches of which, the whole colony may assemble to deliberate on public matters. It is more than probable that their first laws will have the title only of regulations, and be enforced by no other penalty than public disfavor. In this first parliament every man, by natural right, will have a seat.

Note : Only spelling mistakes, if any, in the above passage has been corrected. No other corrections, including grammatical, have been made so that the originality of the passage is maintained.

Name ______________________________ Date ________________

1. Match the following statements to either society or government as they are described in the passage.

	Society	Government
Brings together what we like	○	○
Holds in our evil	○	○
Created by our desires	○	○
Produced by mischief	○	○

2. What is the theme in "Common Sense"? Use evidence from the text to support your ideas.

3. After reading paragraph 3 of the passage, what do you think the author has included to describe how the government would want to be built by the citizens themselves?

4. Describe the connection Thomas Paine makes between the government and it's citizens.

5. What claim about the government is expressed by the author in the passage?

Ⓐ The government should look to other governments for structure.
Ⓑ The government harms its citizens who work hard.
Ⓒ The government lacks the proper protocol to function.
Ⓓ The government spends inappropriately using its funds.

6. What were the results of Thomas Paine's writing "Common Sense"?

Name ______________________ Date ______________

Passage 8: Declaration of Independence

Directions: Read the excerpt from "The Declaration of Independence" and the copy of Thomas Jefferson's Handwritten Rough Draft of the Declaration of Independence. Then answer the questions.

The history of the present King of Great Britain is a history of repeated injuries and seizures, all having in direct object the establishment of an absolute Tyranny over these States. To prove this, let Facts be submitted to a candid world.

He has refused his Assent to Laws, the most wholesome and necessary for the public good.

He has forbidden his Governors to pass Laws of immediate and pressing importance, unless suspended in their operation till his Assent should be obtained; and when so suspended, he has utterly neglected to attend to them.

He has refused to pass other Laws for the accommodation of large districts of people, unless those people would relinquish the right of Representation in the Legislature, a right inestimable to them and formidable to tyrants only.

He has called together legislative bodies at places unusual, uncomfortable, and distant from the depository of their Public Records, for the sole purpose of fatiguing them into compliance with his measures.

He has dissolved Representative Houses repeatedly, for opposing with manly firmness his invasions on the rights of the people.

He has refused for a long time, after such dissolutions, to cause others to be elected; whereby the Legislative Powers, incapable of Annihilation, have returned to the People at large for their exercise; the State remaining in the meantime exposed to all the dangers of invasion from without, and convulsions within.

He has endeavored to prevent the population of these States; for that purpose obstructing the Laws of Naturalization of Foreigners; refusing to pass others to encourage their migration hither, and raising the conditions of new Appropriations of Lands.

Note

Only spelling mistakes, if any, in the above passage has been corrected. No other corrections, including grammatical, have been made so that the originality of the passage is maintained.

Name ______________________ Date ______________

1. **Match the following details to their central idea.**

	Disagreement of needed regulations	Did not use parts of Parliament bodies	Useless meetings
dissolved Representative Houses repeatedly	○	○	○
refused his Assent to Laws	○	○	○
called together legislative bodies at places unusual, uncomfortable, and distant	○	○	○

2. **What word best describes Jefferson's attitude and point of view towards the British government? Write the correct answer in the box below.**

Ⓐ Bitter
Ⓑ Callous
Ⓒ Detached
Ⓓ Egotistical

3. **Which words in the rough draft seem to be the most important based on their appearance?**

Ⓐ When in the course of human events
Ⓑ United States of America
Ⓒ Declaration
Ⓓ Independence

Name ______________________________ Date ______________

4. Comparing the rough draft with the published copy of the "Declaration of Independence,", Jefferson made many ______________________________.

5. Most likely the most difficult section to write using the rough draft would be ______________________________.

Passage 9: The Underground Railroad

Her husband, William, was thoroughly colored but was a man of marked natural abilities of good manners, and full of pluck and possessed of perceptive faculties very large.

It was necessary, however, in those days that they should seek a permanent residence where their freedom would be more secure than in Philadelphia. Therefore, they were advised to go to headquarters directly to Boston. There they would be safe it was supposed as it had then been about a generation since a fugitive had been taken back from the old Bay State and through the incessant labors of William Lloyd Garrison, the great pioneer, and his faithful assistant, it was conceded that another fugitive slave case could never be tolerated on the free soil of Massachusetts. So, to Boston they went.

On arriving, the warm hearts of abolitionists welcomed them heartily and greeted and cheered them without let or hindrance. They did not pretend to keep their coming a secret or hide it under a bushel. The story of their escape was heralded broadcast over the country—North and South, and indeed over the civilized world. For two years or more, not the slightest fear was entertained that they were not just as safe in Boston as if they had gone to Canada. But the day the Fugitive Bill passed, even the bravest abolitionist began to fear that a fugitive slave was no longer safe anywhere under the stars and stripes, North or South, and that William and Ellen Craft were liable to be captured at any moment by Georgia slave hunters. Many abolitionists counselled resistance to the death at all hazards. Instead of running to Canada, fugitives generally armed themselves and thus said, "Give me liberty or give me death."

William and Ellen Craft believed that it was their duty as citizens of Massachusetts to observe a more legal and civilized mode of conforming to the marriage rite than had been permitted them in slavery, and as Theodore Parker had shown himself a very warm friend of theirs, they agreed to have their wedding over again according to the laws of a free State. After performing the ceremony, the renowned and fearless advocate of equal rights (Theodore Parker), presented William with a revolver and a dirk-knife, counselling him to use them manfully in defense of his wife and himself if ever an attempt should be made by his owners or anybody else to re-enslave them.

But, not withstanding all the published declarations made by abolitionists and fugitives, to the effect, that slave-holders and slave-catchers in visiting Massachusetts in pursuit of their runaway property would be met by just such weapons as Theodore Parker presented William with to the surprise of all Boston the owners of William and Ellen actually had the boldness to attempt their recapture under the Fugitive Slave Law.

Note

Only spelling mistakes, if any, in the above passage has been corrected. No other corrections, including grammatical, have been made so that the originality of the passage is maintained.

Name ______________________ Date ______________

1. The central idea of the Craft's fear of the Fugitive Slave Law emerges when ______________.

2. How does the meaning of the Fugitive Slave Law affect the central idea?

Ⓐ It explains that only Philadelphia was affected by the Fugitive Slave Law.
Ⓑ It explains a law that was put in place after the Crafts escaped.
Ⓒ It shows that the law was enacted after the Crafts had run away.
Ⓓ It shows that the Crafts' journey was never complete.

3. Why did the author write this passage in chronological order?

Name ______________________ Date ______________

4. **What is the connection between the former slave owners and the Fugitive Slave Law?**

5. **How is the author's claim shown through the actions of William and Ellen Craft?**

Ⓐ By revealing the fear the Crafts must have felt from the Fugitive Slave Law.
Ⓑ By showing how the couple was able to make it to freedom.
Ⓒ By providing examples of ways the Crafts helped others to freedom.
Ⓓ By showing how the Crafts knew which city to travel to.

6. **How does the second paragraph fit into the passage?**

7. What is the author's purpose of this passage?

Ⓐ to inform the reader about a certain aspect of the Underground Railroad
Ⓑ to show how the Underground Railroad worked through one couple's journey
Ⓒ to reveal how the Fugitive Slave Law could return slaves who made their way to the free states
Ⓓ to describe William and Ellen Craft's life

Name ______________________ Date ______________

Passage 10: The True Story of Our National Calamity of Flood, Fire and Tornado

With the rest of the country, fair Dayton sorrowed for Omaha. Two days later Omaha, bowed and almost broken by her own misfortune, looked with sympathy across to Dayton, whose woe was even greater. A thousand communities in the United States read the story and in their own sense of security sent eager volunteers of assistance to the stricken districts. Not one of them has assurance that it may not be next. There is no sure definition of the course of the earthquake, the path of the wind, or the time and place of the storm-cloud. Science has its limitations.

In the legal jargon of the practice of torts such occurrences as these are known as "acts of God." Theologians who attempt to solve the mysteries of Providence have found in such occasions the evidence of Divine wrath and warning to the smitten people. But to seek the reason and to know the purpose, if there be purpose in it, is not necessary. The fact is enough. It challenges, staggers, calls a halt, compels men and women to think—and even to pray.

But the flood did not confine itself to Dayton. It laid its watery hand of death and destruction over a whole tier of states from the Great Lakes to New England, and over the vast area to the southward which is veined by the Ohio River and its tributaries, and extending from the Mississippi Valley almost to the Atlantic seaboard. And as this awful deluge drained from the land into Nature's watercourses the demons of death and devastation danced attendance on its mad rush that laid waste the borderlands of the Mississippi River from Illinois to the Gulf of Mexico.

Those who have never seen a great flood do not know the meaning of the Scriptural phrase, "the abomination of desolation."

An explosion, a railroad wreck, even a fire—these are bad enough in their pictorial effect of shattered ruins and confusion. But for giving one an oppressive sense of death-like misery, there is nothing equal to a flood.

I do not speak now of the loss of life, which is unspeakably dreadful, but of the scenic effect of the disaster. It just grips and benumbs you with its awfulness.

In the flat country of the Middle West there is less likelihood of swift, complete destruction than in narrow valleys, like those of Johnstown and Austin in Pennsylvania. But the effect is, if anything, more gruesome.

After the crest has passed there are miles and miles of inundated land, with only trees and half- submerged buildings and floating wreckage to break the monotony; just a vast lake of yellow, muddy water, swirling and boiling as it seeks to find its level.

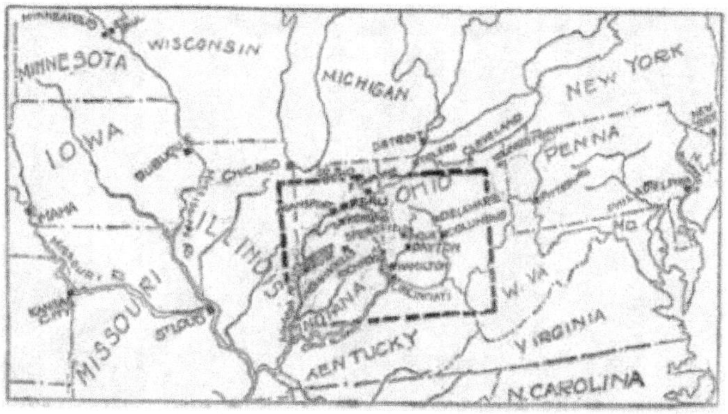

THE CITIES AND TOWNS INCLOSED BY THE HEAVY BLACK DOTTED LINES WERE THE CHIEF SUFFERERS BY THE SWEEP OF WATERS

Note : Only spelling mistakes, if any, in the above passage has been corrected. No other corrections, including grammatical, have been made so that the originality of the passage is maintained.

Name ______________________________ Date ________________

1. What does the author do to develop his ideas about the destruction of flooding?

2. Describe the author's claim about the flooding that took place.

3. How does the fifth paragraph contribute to the claim about flooding?

Name ______________________ Date ______________

4. How does the author feel about the severity of the flooding?

5. Which statement is true about the map?

Ⓐ It displays how the lowest part of the country is located near Ohio.
Ⓑ It shows that major cities like Chicago and New York City were not affected.
Ⓒ It reveals that most of the affected cities are located in a small area of the U.S.
Ⓓ It provides a visual about where the main flooding devastation took place.

6. Observe the map shown at the end of the passage.

Why does the author include the black dotted lines, representing water?

7. Observe the map shown at the end of the passage.

How does the map support the information in the passage?

Ⓐ It pinpoints the key places described in the passage that was heavily flooded.
Ⓑ It shows a general picture of the flooding that was revealed in the passage.
Ⓒ It makes a connection between the ways that people could have helped those who were affected.
Ⓓ The map shows certain places like the Middle West and where it is located.

8. Match the items that are found on the map as important/not important to the information in the passage.

	Important to the information in the passage	**Not important to the information in the passage**
location of rivers in comparison to the flooding	○	○
states' borders	○	○
location of Dayton, Ohio and its surrounding cities	○	○

Name ______________________________ Date ________________

Language Standards

This Covers standards from L.9-10.1 to L.9-10.6

Lesson 1 : Grammar and Usage Conventions

1. "Jim's brand new sports car skidded to a stop in the driveway."

In the quote above, which words represent a verb phrase?

Ⓐ Jim's brand new sports car
Ⓑ skidded to a stop
Ⓒ in the driveway
Ⓓ None of the above

2. "Jim's brand new sports car skidded to a stop in the driveway."

In the quote above, which words represent a noun phrase?

Ⓐ Jim's brand new sports car
Ⓑ skidded to a stop
Ⓒ in the driveway
Ⓓ None of the above

3. "Jim's brand new sports car skidded to a stop in the driveway."

In the quote above, which words represent a prepositional phrase?

Ⓐ Jim's brand new sports car
Ⓑ skidded to a stop
Ⓒ in the driveway
Ⓓ None of the above

4. Which of the following is a sentence fragment?

Ⓐ Xiomara was late for class.
Ⓑ When Jared went home.
Ⓒ After Rachel took her test, she drew a picture.
Ⓓ Because of the thunderstorm, the game was cancelled.

5. The dog, which came from the local animal shelter, dug holes in the yard. In the quote above, "which came from the local animal shelter" functions as a(n)

Ⓐ independent clause
Ⓑ dependent clause
Ⓒ relative clause
Ⓓ verbal phrase

6. Identify the problem with this sentence: "Smith forgot to feed the dog, his mom was disappointed."

Ⓐ comma splice
Ⓑ run on
Ⓒ sentence fragment
Ⓓ faulty parallelism

7. Complete the sentence: "The twins' mother enjoyed going to the store and _________."

Ⓐ buy matching outfits for the sisters.
Ⓑ bought matching outfits for the sisters.
Ⓒ will buy matching outfits for the sisters.
Ⓓ buying matching outfits for the sisters.

8. Which of the following sentences has an absolute phrase?

Ⓐ Afraid of what her dad might think, Stacy decided not to tell the truth.
Ⓑ After the game ended, my parents drove me home.
Ⓒ When I found my car keys, it was too late to go to the party.
Ⓓ Looking out the window is one of my favorite ways to pass the time.

9. **What punctuation should be used to divide the two independent clauses?**
The appointment was scheduled for this afternoon but we were late getting back into town.

Ⓐ period (.)
Ⓑ comma (,)
Ⓒ colon (:)
Ⓓ semicolon (;)

10. **"We went to Dallas, and we went to San Antonio."**

What is the above sentence an example of?

Ⓐ sentence fragment
Ⓑ run on
Ⓒ comma splice
Ⓓ parallel structure

Name ______________________ Date ______________

Lesson 2 : Capitalization, Punctuation, and Spelling

1. Which of the following does not need to be capitalized in a sentence?

Ⓐ first letter in the sentence
Ⓑ proper nouns
Ⓒ common nouns
Ⓓ acronyms

2. Correct the run-on: "The company's expenses went over budget in February spending was reduced in March." Write the correct answer in the below box.

Ⓐ The company's expenses went over budget in February, spending was reduced in March.
Ⓑ The company's expenses went over budget in February; therefore, spending was reduced in March.
Ⓒ The company's expenses went over budget in February: spending was reduced in March.
Ⓓ No change.

3. How should you correct the following sentence?

Your one of the top performers on the team, which is why you're contribution is so important.

4. Name the type of error in the following sentence:

"The whether outside was getting damp and muggy."

Ⓐ capitalization
Ⓑ punctuation
Ⓒ homophone usage
Ⓓ sentence fragment

Name ______________________ Date ____________

5. A __________ is when two independent clauses are combined by a comma without a coordinating conjunction.

Ⓐ sentence fragment
Ⓑ run on
Ⓒ compound sentence
Ⓓ comma splice

6. Which of the following does not use a comma correctly?

Ⓐ When I got home from school, I had to finish my homework before I played video games.
Ⓑ When I got home from school, I had to finish my homework, before I played video games.
Ⓒ Before I played video games, I had to finish my homework when I got home from school.
Ⓓ I had to finish my homework before I played video games when I got home from school.

7. Correct the following sentence: "Her brother spent to much time talking too his girlfriend."

Ⓐ Her brother spent two much time talking too his girlfriend.
Ⓑ Her brother spent too much time talking too his girlfriend.
Ⓒ Her brother spent too much time talking two his girlfriend.
Ⓓ Her brother spent too much time talking to his girlfriend.

8. Read the following two sentences:

1. The president prepared for a press conference.

2. The audience applauded when President Obama spoke.

Why is "president" capitalized in one sentence but not the other?

Name ______________________________ Date ______________

9. Identify the sentence that has a spelling error.

Ⓐ The students found the schedule for the weekend to be exceptable.
Ⓑ The effect the food had on the customers was concerning.
Ⓒ The acceptable time to meet was around noon.
Ⓓ The medicine affected her differently than most people.

10. Words that are pronounced the same but are spelled differently are called __________.

11. A ___________ can be used before a list of items in a series.

Ⓐ comma
Ⓑ semicolon
Ⓒ period
Ⓓ colon

12. Match the figure of speech with its definition.

Homophones	
Homonyms	
Homographs	
Synonyms	
Antonyms	

1. A word that has the same sound as another word but its spelling and meanings are different
2. A word that is spelled like another word but it has a different sound and meaning
3. A word whose meaning is same as given word
4. A word whose meaning is opposite of given word
5. Words which have the same sound or spelling but have different meaning

Lesson 3 : Functions of Language

1. Select the title of the source in this Works Cited entry for an article. Beck, Julie, "The Psychology of Voldemort", The Atlantic, 23 Sept. 2015.

Ⓐ Julie Beck
Ⓑ The Psychology of Voldemort
Ⓒ The Atlantic
Ⓓ September 23, 2015

2. Select the author of the source in this Works Cited entry for an article. Beck, Julie, "The Psychology of Voldemort", The Atlantic, 23 Sept. 2015.

Ⓐ Julie Beck
Ⓑ The Psychology of Voldemort
Ⓒ The Atlantic
Ⓓ Beck, Julie

3. Complete the following analogy: Trustworthy is to credible as faulty is to ________.

Ⓐ strong
Ⓑ fallible
Ⓒ reliable
Ⓓ conclusive

4. Select the author of the source in this Works Cited entry for a book. Snow, Shane, *Smartcuts*, New York, HarperBusiness 2014.

Ⓐ Shane Snow
Ⓑ Smartcuts
Ⓒ New York
Ⓓ HarperBusiness

5. Select the title of the source in this Works Cited entry for a book. Snow, Shane, *Smartcuts*, New York, HarperBusiness 2014.

Ⓐ Shane Snow
Ⓑ Smartcuts
Ⓒ New York
Ⓓ HarperBusiness

Name ______________________________ Date ______________

6. **Why is it important to use a variety of sentence structures?**

7. **Anna is writing a research paper on The Illiad for her English class. Which style guide should she use?**

Ⓐ The Chicago Manual of Style
Ⓑ The Associated Press Stylebook
Ⓒ The MLA Handbook
Ⓓ A Manual for Writers of Term Papers, Theses, and Dissertations, by Kate L. Turabian

8. **Jared wants to write an article about a local restaurant owner for his town's newspaper. Which style guide should he use?**

Ⓐ The Chicago Manual of Style
Ⓑ The Associated Press Stylebook
Ⓒ The MLA Handbook
Ⓓ A Manual for Writers of Term Papers, Theses, and Dissertations, by Kate L. Turabian

9. **Another name for the Works Cited page is ______________**

Ⓐ List of Sources
Ⓑ Sources Consulted
Ⓒ Research
Ⓓ Bibliography

10. **Why is it important to use an up-to-date style guide rather than one published before the Internet became widely used?**

Name ______________________ Date ______________

Lesson 4 : Determining Unknown Words

1. Overconfident, overburdened, and overjoyed all begin with the prefix over-. What is the meaning of the prefix over-? Write the correct answer in the below box.

Ⓐ beneath
Ⓑ excessively
Ⓒ around
Ⓓ above

2. Which word is a synonym for accentuate?

Ⓐ decorate
Ⓑ hide
Ⓒ reflect
Ⓓ highlight

3. Which prefix means against?

Ⓐ mis-
Ⓑ anti-
Ⓒ non-
Ⓓ un-

4. Which root word means sound?

Ⓐ alter
Ⓑ carn
Ⓒ aud
Ⓓ arch

5. Which suffix means belief?

Ⓐ -er
Ⓑ -ness
Ⓒ -tion
Ⓓ -ism

Name ______________________ Date ______________

6. **Which root word means writing or printing?**

Ⓐ graph-
Ⓑ demo-
Ⓒ grad-
Ⓓ lect-

7. **Though Jennifer tried to get the team to support her decision, most of them disagreed with her. In the word disagreed in the sentence above, the prefix dis- most likely means**

Ⓐ between
Ⓑ very
Ⓒ not
Ⓓ reduce

8. **Gene, generate, and generous all include the root word gen. What is the meaning of the root word gen?**

Ⓐ To lead
Ⓑ To make
Ⓒ To birth
Ⓓ To feel

9. **A(n) ________ is a letter or group of letters added to the end of a word to change its meaning.**

Ⓐ prefix
Ⓑ suffix
Ⓒ root word
Ⓓ none of the above

10. **After all of the misfortune she went through over the past year, Angela couldn't help but feel despondent. Based on the context of the sentence above, the word despondent most likely means**

Ⓐ without hope
Ⓑ full of hope
Ⓒ unlucky
Ⓓ fortunate

Name ______________________ Date ______________

Lesson 5 : Figurative Language

1. Choose the correct answer.

	inexpensive	cheap
Which word has the more positive connotation?	○	○

2. Choose the correct answer.

	home	shack
Which word has the more negative connotation?	○	○

3. "Old news" is an example of which type of figurative language?

Ⓐ metaphor
Ⓑ simile
Ⓒ onomatopoeia
Ⓓ oxymoron

4. The rain sounded like small pellets falling onto the roof.

Which type of figurative language does the sentence above use?

Ⓐ metaphor
Ⓑ simile
Ⓒ hyperbole
Ⓓ personification

5. The clouds sobbed, drenching the earth with their tears. Which type of figurative language does the sentence above use?

Ⓐ metaphor
Ⓑ simile
Ⓒ hyperbole
Ⓓ personification

6. Choose the correct answer.

	casual	apathetic
Which word has the more positive connotation?	○	○

7. Elmer could hear the sound of freedom echoing in his ears every time he revved the car's engine. Which type of figurative language does the sentence above use?

Ⓐ metaphor
Ⓑ simile
Ⓒ hyperbole
Ⓓ personification

8. The song played forever, and I desperately wanted it to stop.

The sentence above uses which type of figurative language?

Ⓐ personification
Ⓑ metaphor
Ⓒ simile
Ⓓ hyperbole

9. When Martin Luther King, Jr. begins his famous "I Have a Dream" speech with the words "Five score years ago," he is making a(n) ______________ to a speech made by Abraham Lincoln.

10. A ___________ is a dictionary definition of a word, and a ____________ is meaning associated with the word outside of its dictionary definition.

Name ______________________________ Date ________________

Lesson 6 : Academic and Domain-Specific Vocabulary

1. **Select the word that best completes the sentence given below:**

   "The football team we are playing this Friday hasn't lost a game yet, making them a(n) __________ opponent."

   Ⓐ acceptable
   Ⓑ formidable
   Ⓒ credible
   Ⓓ reasonable

2. **Select the word that best completes the sentence given below:**

   "When Sara felt alone, she struggled to feel better about herself, but when she began to make friends at school, her personality began to ___________."

   Ⓐ exult
   Ⓑ maneuver
   Ⓒ flourish
   Ⓓ descend

3. **Select the word that best completes the sentence given below:**

   "Chad didn't feel like celebrating when he woke up this morning, but when all his friends surprised him with a party for his birthday, he felt more ___________."

   Ⓐ jovial
   Ⓑ melancholy
   Ⓒ laconic
   Ⓓ random

4. **Select the word that best completes the sentence given below:**

   "The citywide vote last year to increase taxes to increase teacher pay was divided, but the vote was __________ this year, which will be good news for teachers."

   Ⓐ voracious
   Ⓑ receded
   Ⓒ reposed
   Ⓓ unanimous

5. **Select the word that best completes the sentence given below: "My appetite was ___________ after going without food for two days."**

Ⓐ voracious
Ⓑ quenched
Ⓒ tumultuous
Ⓓ wretched

6. **The main character of a story is known as the _____**

Ⓐ antagonist
Ⓑ foil
Ⓒ protagonist
Ⓓ narrator

7. **Select the word that best completes the sentence given below:**

"To discover who committed the crime, the investigator will have to ____________ all of the evidence."

Ⓐ infer
Ⓑ estimate
Ⓒ assess
Ⓓ analyze

8. **Select the word that best completes the sentence given below:**

"Determining the meaning of the word often requires first looking at the surrounding _________ of the word."

Ⓐ concept
Ⓑ climax
Ⓒ context
Ⓓ characterization

Name ________________________ Date ______________

9. Select the word that best completes the sentence given below:

"Since Susan didn't need to know the exact amount of pizzas to purchase to feed everyone, she decided to make a(n) __________."

Ⓐ assessment
Ⓑ estimate
Ⓒ announcement
Ⓓ deduction

10. Select the word that best completes the sentence given below:

"Most of the time, you can accurately ___________ a person's character based off of their actions and the way they treat others."

Ⓐ doubt
Ⓑ analyze
Ⓒ recede
Ⓓ assess

Name ______________________ Date ______________

Writing Standards

This Covers standards from W.9-10.1 to W.9-10.10

Lesson 1 : Writing Arguments

1. Which of the following is the best thesis statement for an argumentative essay?

Ⓐ Gap years are becoming more and more popular among high school graduates.
Ⓑ This essay is going to be about the benefits of gap years.
Ⓒ Although high school graduates have traditionally entered college directly after graduation, there are a number of reasons to consider taking a gap year instead.
Ⓓ Gap years are helpful.

2. An argumentative thesis statement must do all of the following EXCEPT?

Ⓐ Make a claim
Ⓑ Be debatable
Ⓒ Be an opinion
Ⓓ State a fact

3. The part of your argument that considers what the opposition has to say is called?

Ⓐ call to action
Ⓑ counterclaim
Ⓒ thesis statement
Ⓓ claim

4. Which of the following should you include in the conclusion of your argument?

Ⓐ Evidence
Ⓑ Call to action
Ⓒ Counterclaim
Ⓓ claim

5. Which of the following maintains a formal style and objective tone?

Ⓐ The folks enrolled at the local university helped them do some research.
Ⓑ The students of the prestigious institution participated in a unique research study.
Ⓒ The kids at the best college in town were part of an experiment.
Ⓓ The college kids helped with the research.

6. In which part of your argument should you include a call to action?

Ⓐ In the introduction
Ⓑ In the thesis Statement
Ⓒ In the body
Ⓓ In the conclusion

7. Match the following as credible source or non-credible source used to support a claim.

	Credible Source	Non credible source
Wikipedia entry	○	○
A scientific journal article	○	○
A high school student's blog	○	○
A friend's opinion about a topic	○	○

8. Which of the following is a claim for an argument?

Ⓐ Classrooms should have tables instead of desks to promote more student collaboration.
Ⓑ I personally like being in a classroom with tables.
Ⓒ Most classrooms have rows of desks.
Ⓓ Have you ever been in a classroom where group work was encouraged?

9. What types of evidence best support a claim?

Ⓐ Logical reasoning
Ⓑ Statistics
Ⓒ Quotes from experts
Ⓓ All of the above

Name ______________________ Date ____________

10. Why should you consider a target audience when writing an argument?

Lesson 2 : Informational Writing

1. Which of the following would be an example of informational writing?

Ⓐ A story about an evil queen
Ⓑ A newspaper report about a local fair
Ⓒ A presentation to convince the school board to change the school start time
Ⓓ A poem about a struggling friendship

2. What pattern of organization does the author use in the passage below?

Jayden wondered why he wasn't able to stay awake during class recently. The more he thought about it, the more he realized he was probably spending too much time playing his video games at night before going to bed.

Ⓐ Problem and solution
Ⓑ Compare and contrast
Ⓒ Cause and effect
Ⓓ Order of importance

3. What pattern of organization does the author use in the passage below?

Trash build-up in the local parks is a serious problem. Local service groups, however, can make a difference by just spending an hour each week picking up trash.

Ⓐ Problem and solution
Ⓑ Compare and contrast
Ⓒ Cause and effect
Ⓓ Order of importance

4. What pattern of organization does the author use in the passage below?

Writing an essay isn't that hard if you follow a process. First, you should brainstorm some ideas until you find something you're confident you can write well about. Then, you can develop a clear controlling idea for your essay. Follow this with an outline of your thoughts on the controlling idea, then write your first draft. Finally, you'll revise and edit your draft until it's ready for submission.

Ⓐ Problem and solution
Ⓑ Compare and contrast
Ⓒ Cause and effect
Ⓓ Order of importance

Name ______________________ Date ______________

5. **What pattern of organization does the author use in the passage below?**

Desktop computers and laptop computers both perform a lot of the same functions. For example, you can pull up a word processing program on either device and type up a report or send an email. Laptops, however, are often preferred by busy people who are always on the go because they can take their computer with them and work from anywhere. Desktop computers, though they often have more power and space, don't provide the convenience of laptop computers.

Ⓐ Problem and solution
Ⓑ Compare and contrast
Ⓒ Cause and effect
Ⓓ Order of importance

6. **What pattern of organization should the author use if she is writing about how to fix the current issues faced by students who have too much homework?**

Ⓐ Problem and solution
Ⓑ Compare and contrast
Ⓒ Cause and effect
Ⓓ Order of importance

7. **Which transition would be appropriate in the passage below?**

The Rams won every game in the regular season and seemed poised to win the championship. The Patriots, ______________, didn't win every game, but they played each game with heart and strategy.

Ⓐ for example
Ⓑ consequently
Ⓒ however
Ⓓ in fact

8. **What organizational structure would you use if you were writing about a memory of when you received your best gift?**

Ⓐ Problem and solution
Ⓑ Chronological
Ⓒ Cause and effect
Ⓓ Compare and contrast

9. **What organizational structure would you use if you were writing a guide on how to recycle?**

Ⓐ Problem and solution
Ⓑ Compare and contrast
Ⓒ Cause and effect
Ⓓ Order of importance

Lesson 3 : Writing Narratives

1. The character the reader is most meant to identify within a story is known as the:

Ⓐ foil
Ⓑ protagonist
Ⓒ antagonist
Ⓓ sidekick

2. What point of view does the author use in the passage below?

Jack wondered if Sarah knew what secrets he held from his childhood. She didn't seem to treat him any differently, but still he wondered.

Ⓐ Third person objective
Ⓑ First person
Ⓒ Third person omniscient
Ⓓ Third person limited

3. The part of a story that establishes the setting and the characters is known as:

Ⓐ the exposition
Ⓑ the rising action
Ⓒ the climax
Ⓓ the resolution

4. When a narrative is interrupted by a scene that occurred earlier in time, the scene is known as a/an:

Ⓐ foreshadowing
Ⓑ rising action
Ⓒ flashback
Ⓓ exposition

5. A character who stays the same from the beginning of the story to the end is:

Ⓐ dynamic
Ⓑ flat
Ⓒ static
Ⓓ round

Name ______________________ Date ______________

6. **Match the pronoun to the point of view.**

	First Person	Second Person	Third Person
I, We	◯	◯	◯
Me, Us	◯	◯	◯
He, she, it	◯	◯	◯
You, yours	◯	◯	◯

7. **What type of conflict is it known as, when a character struggles internally with a major life decision in a story?**

Ⓐ Person versus person
Ⓑ Person versus nature
Ⓒ Person versus himself/herself
Ⓓ Person versus society

8. **An author will often plant clues in the early part of a story that gives the reader a hint about something to come later. What is this technique known as?**

Ⓐ foreshadowing
Ⓑ rising action
Ⓒ flashback
Ⓓ exposition

9. **Think of all the post-apocalyptic stories that have become popular in recent years. Write a short story about a post-apocalyptic event and how it occurred to change the world.**

10. **The type of character who undergoes change in a story is known as?**

Ⓐ dynamic
Ⓑ flat
Ⓒ static
Ⓓ round

Name ______________________ Date ______________

Lesson 4 : Produce Clear and Coherent Writing

1. What is the purpose of the paragraph below?
Bats are the only mammals that fly. They're surprisingly clean animals, spending a majority of their time cleaning their fur.

Ⓐ Persuade
Ⓑ Entertain
Ⓒ Inform
Ⓓ None of the above

2. What purpose of the sentence below?

If you've never visited London, you should plan to go at least once. The city streets are breathtaking, and you'll love British culture.

Ⓐ To Persuade
Ⓑ To Entertain
Ⓒ To Inform
Ⓓ None of the above

3. Which of the following sentences is written correctly?

Ⓐ We wanted to take the bus to the city but Jeremy called to say that he wood be late.
Ⓑ We wanted to take the bus to the city, but Jeremy called to say that he would be late
Ⓒ We wanted to take the bus to the city, but Jeremy called to say that he would be late.
Ⓓ we wanted to take the bus to the city but Jeremy called to say that he would be late.

4. True or false?

	True	False
Narratives often use an informal style of writing.	○	○

5. Which of the following should be capitalized in a piece of writing?

Ⓐ The beginning letter of a sentence
Ⓑ Proper nouns
Ⓒ Titles
Ⓓ All of the above

6. Billy wants to write a letter to the school board, requesting an upgrade to the school's cafeteria tables. What type of writing will this be?

Ⓐ Informational
Ⓑ Argumentative
Ⓒ A Narrative
Ⓓ None of the above

7. Jennifer wants to write about when she got her first pet. What type of writing will this be?

Ⓐ Informational
Ⓑ Argumentative
Ⓒ A Narrative
Ⓓ None of the above

8. "Samuel wants to write about the issue of water pollution in the Earth's oceans and share some of his ideas for eliminating pollution. Which organizational pattern will best serve Samuel's writing purpose? "

Ⓐ Cause and effect
Ⓑ Compare and contrast
Ⓒ Sequential
Ⓓ Problem and solution

9. Which of the following sentences is written correctly?

Ⓐ Because of you, I know I can have an affect on someone.
Ⓑ Because of you, I know I can have a effect on someone.
Ⓒ Because of you I know I can have a affect on someone.
Ⓓ Because of you, I know I can have an effect on someone.

10. Which organizational pattern would be best for giving someone instructions on how to replace a broken light switch?

Ⓐ Problem and solution
Ⓑ Compare and contrast
Ⓒ Cause and effect
Ⓓ Order of importance

Name ______________________________ Date ________________

Lesson 5 : Develop and Strengthen Writing

1. Which of the following is a simple sentence?

Ⓐ The dog ran away and found his previous owners.
Ⓑ The dog ran away, but we found him.
Ⓒ The dog ran away because I forgot to close the gate.
Ⓓ Because I forgot to close the gate, the dog ran away, but we found him.

2. Which of the following is a compound sentence?

Ⓐ Sam hates doing homework even though her parents push her to do her best.
Ⓑ Sam hates doing homework, but her parents push her to do her best.
Ⓒ Sam hates doing homework and disappointing her parents.
Ⓓ Sam hates doing homework until she goes to sleep, but her parents push her to do her best.

3. Which sentence uses an introductory phrase correctly?

Ⓐ After the game ended, we went to the pizza restaurant.
Ⓑ After the game, we went to the pizza restaurant.
Ⓒ After the game ended we went to the pizza restaurant.
Ⓓ After the game we went to the pizza restaurant.

4. Which of the following is NOT a part of the editing stage of the writing process?

Ⓐ Looking over grammar
Ⓑ Checking capitalization
Ⓒ Replacing weak verbs with stronger verbs
Ⓓ Proofreading punctuation

5. Which of the following is NOT a part of the revision stage of the writing process?

Ⓐ Reordering paragraphs
Ⓑ Revising sentences for variety
Ⓒ Correcting spelling mistakes
Ⓓ Adding information

Name ______________________ Date ______________

6. **Which of the following sentences would benefit from proofreading?**

Ⓐ Your performance this semester has been exemplary.
Ⓑ Your one of the top performers in the class.
Ⓒ Your attitude drives others to perform better.
Ⓓ Your future looks bright.

7. **Which sentence below is strengthened by using an active verb?**

Ⓐ The snake was in the yard.
Ⓑ The snake has been in the yard.
Ⓒ The snake is in the yard.
Ⓓ The snake slithered in the yard.

8. **Where should the thesis statement appear in a piece of writing?**

Ⓐ In the middle
Ⓑ In the first sentence
Ⓒ In the conclusion
Ⓓ In the first paragraph

9. **The sentence that tells the reader what a paragraph will be about is known as the _____**

Ⓐ topic sentence
Ⓑ call to action
Ⓒ supporting detail
Ⓓ thesis statement

10. **Which sentence below has an error in spelling?**

Ⓐ Evelyn's grade on the test was exceptional.
Ⓑ John's favorite animal to study is the kangaruu.
Ⓒ Demetria drove Alex to the stadium.
Ⓓ The embarrassment of the loss was overwhelming.

Name ______________________________ Date ______________

Lesson 6 : Using Technology

1. Which of the following is a correct parenthetical citation in MLA?

Ⓐ Later on, he reflected on his past by saying, "Turning to the Dark Side seemed like the only way I could stop the pain I knew was coming" (There and Back Again 83).
Ⓑ Later on, he reflected on his past by saying, "Turning to the Dark Side seemed like the only way I could stop the pain I knew was coming" (Skywalker 83).
Ⓒ Later on, he reflected on his past by saying, "Turning to the Dark Side seemed like the only way I could stop the pain I knew was coming." (Skywalker 83)
Ⓓ Later on, he reflected on his past by saying, "Turning to the Dark Side seemed like the only way I could stop the pain I knew was coming." (Skywalker 83).

2. MLA stands for

Ⓐ Modern Language Association
Ⓑ Modern Language Arts
Ⓒ Main Linguistic Association
Ⓓ Multiple Language Assets

3. Which of the following is appropriate software to type your writing?

Ⓐ Google Documents
Ⓑ Microsoft Word
Ⓒ Apple Pages
Ⓓ All of the above

4. Taking information from a source and putting it into your own words is known as ____

Ⓐ quoting
Ⓑ summarizing
Ⓒ paraphrasing
Ⓓ phrasing

5. Information quoted from a source must be cited.

True or False?

Name ______________________ Date ______________

6. Why is it important to cite your sources in your writing?

7. Which of the following is an example of plagiarism?

Ⓐ Melissa quotes a psychologist and mentions him by name.
Ⓑ Jacob paraphrases an expert and gives a parenthetical citation for the source.
Ⓒ Miguel writes several paragraphs with his own thoughts on a subject.
Ⓓ Lauren includes information from a scientific journal without citing the source.

8. What is a Works Cited page?

Ⓐ Parenthetical information within a paper indicating where you got your information
Ⓑ A numbered list of the resources you used for a project
Ⓒ An alphabetized list of the sources you used for a project
Ⓓ A chronological list of all the work you did on a project

9. What is the preferred font and size for your text in MLA format?

Ⓐ Calibri, 11
Ⓑ Verdana, 10
Ⓒ Times New Roman, 12
Ⓓ Comic Sans, 14

10. "How do you indent the body paragraphs in your text? "

Ⓐ Why would I indent my paragraphs?
Ⓑ Hit the TAB key
Ⓒ Press the spacebar 5 times
Ⓓ Center align the text

Name ______________________ Date ______________

Lesson 7 : Conducting Research

1. Finding sources for a research project should be guided by a clear

Ⓐ thesis statement
Ⓑ topic sentence
Ⓒ controlling idea
Ⓓ inquiry question

2. "Which of the following should you include in a citation of a source on your works cited page?"

Ⓐ Author's name
Ⓑ Title of source
Ⓒ Year of publication
Ⓓ All of the above

3. Which of the following types of writing involves doing research?

Ⓐ A documentary
Ⓑ A scientific article
Ⓒ A biography
Ⓓ All of the above

4. The following inquiry question would be considered too broad:
How does recycling impact the environment?

True or false?

5. How can you determine if a source is credible?

Name ______________________________ Date ______________

6. **During his research, Amad discovers that ocean pollution is resulting in the population of African Sea Turtles to shrink. Based on this information, which organizational structure should he use in his research paper?**

Ⓐ cause and effect
Ⓑ order of importance
Ⓒ chronological
Ⓓ problem and solution

7. **During her research, Tamara discovers that although homelessness is a real crisis in her community, there are several programs available to help homeless individuals and families transition out of their current situation. Based on this information, which organizational structure should she use in her research paper?**

Ⓐ cause and effect
Ⓑ order of importance
Ⓒ chronological
Ⓓ problem and solution

8. **"Which of the following is a more narrowed inquiry question?"**

Ⓐ What are the effects of smartphone use?
Ⓑ What are the long-term negative effects of smartphone use on teenagers?

9. **Answering your inquiry question helps you to develop the __________ of your research paper.**

Ⓐ topic sentence
Ⓑ thesis statement
Ⓒ introduction
Ⓓ conclusion

10. **True or false?**

	True	False
Research begins the moment you search for your first source of information?	◯	◯

Name ______________________ Date ______________

Lesson 8 : Gathering Information

1. Which of the following is considered a primary source?

Ⓐ A biography
Ⓑ An autobiography
Ⓒ An encyclopedia
Ⓓ A documentary

2. Which of the following is considered a secondary source?

Ⓐ An autobiography
Ⓑ A personal letter
Ⓒ An interview
Ⓓ A biography

3. What is the difference between a primary source and a secondary source?

4. What is the primary purpose of an in-text citation?

Ⓐ To tell the reader where the information came from
Ⓑ To remind the author where the information came from
Ⓒ To make an author's text look more aesthetic
Ⓓ To provide the reader with a link to find more information

5. Why is it important to gather relevant information from multiple sources?

Name ______________________________ Date ________________

6. **Which of the following is not a reliable location for searching for authoritative sources?**

Ⓐ Library
Ⓑ Free internet search engine
Ⓒ Encyclopedia
Ⓓ Peer-reviewed journal

7. **A personal diary is an example of a secondary source.**

True or False?

8. **Trevion wants to write a research paper that explores the positive impacts of former President Barack Obama's eight years in the White House. During his research, he discovers five significant contributions Obama's presidency made. Which of the following would be the best way for him to present his information?**

Ⓐ Problem and solution
Ⓑ Compare and contrast
Ⓒ Cause and effect
Ⓓ Chronological

9. **Gianna wants to write an essay about John Steinbeck's approach to writing novels. Which of the following would be a primary source for her to research?**

Ⓐ A Steinbeck biography
Ⓑ An encyclopedia entry on Steinbeck
Ⓒ Steinbeck's journal kept during the writing of a novel
Ⓓ A Steinbeck documentary

10. **Melanie has an informational essay assignment due in her English class. Because she has other homework, she decides to put it off and use an essay her older sister wrote two years before. When she submits the paper to her teacher, who also taught Melanie's sister, as her own work, what will most likely occur?**

Name ________________________________ Date ________________

Lesson 9 : Using Textual Evidence

Smartphones

Use the text below to answer the following questions:

(1) With the current prevalence of smartphones, owned by young and old alike, it might come as a surprise that smartphone technology is a fairly recent development. Steve Jobs, the former CEO and visionary of Apple who died in October 2011 of cancer, revealed the company's first iPhone on January 9, 2007. Combining the ability to make a phone call, text messaging, internet browsing, music streaming, and a number of other capabilities, the iPhone and other smartphones that followed in the iPhone's footsteps quickly became commonplace as the go-to informational access device for people all over the world. Though smartphones offer a significant number of conveniences, the over-reliance on the technology has become a growing concern among teenagers and adults.

(2) In classrooms all over the country, teachers are fighting a battle for the attention of the students in their classes. The opposition? The smartphone with almost unlimited options resting in the students' pockets, or, more likely, in the students' hands. With access to videos, games, and messaging services that allow them to connect with their friends, even if the friend is in the same classroom, students often find their smartphone screen to be more engaging than the lesson on gerunds the teacher has to offer. And though teachers might try to solve the problem by taking up a student's cell phone, a surprising amount of anxiety is felt by the student when he or she is disconnected from the device that makes them feel most connected to the world at large. "Taking it away doesn't solve the problem," said 9th-grade history teacher, Morgan Giles. She continued to say that taking the students' smartphones just created a power struggle. "There has to be a better way," she said.

(3) Studies have also shown that students are spending so much time on their screens that it's affecting their ability to interact with the real world around them. Students are losing sleep from staying up late to play games on their smartphone, according to a study done by American Academy of Sleep Medicine. Even family connections are being negatively impacted by smartphone usage, as families gather around the dinner table, faces buried in their smartphones rather than engaging in conversation with the people around them.

(4) Some might argue that smartphones increase student safety. Having a smartphone, after all, keeps students connected to their parents, and they always have a way to contact authorities at the touch of a button. While these are fair arguments, the benefits don't erase the negative effects teenagers are suffering from the overuse of their smartphones.

(5) While smartphones have certainly made many things more convenient, parents would do well to teach their children how to better handle something so small that asks for so much of their attention.

1. Which of the following best describes the tone of the passage?

Ⓐ Lighthearted
Ⓑ Cautionary
Ⓒ Dire
Ⓓ Melancholy

Name ______________________ Date ______________

2. Briefly summarize the passage.

3. What argument does the author make? Write the correct answer in the box below.

Ⓐ Smartphones provide a number of conveniences to their users.
Ⓑ Smartphones are dangerous and should be eliminated.
Ⓒ Smartphones are designed to be a distraction to their users.
Ⓓ Despite their benefits, smartphones are proving to be a distraction to teenagers.

4. Which paragraph includes the counterclaim?

Ⓐ Paragraph 1
Ⓑ Paragraph 2
Ⓒ Paragraph 3
Ⓓ Paragraph 4

5. What kind of evidence does the author use to support his argument?

Name ______________________ Date ______________

6. **In addition to restating the author's claim, what does a paragraph serve to give the reader?**

Ⓐ Exposition
Ⓑ Evidence
Ⓒ Counterclaim
Ⓓ Call to Action

7. **How does the author present the information in Paragraphs 2 and 3?**

Ⓐ Problem and solution
Ⓑ Compare and contrast
Ⓒ Cause and effect
Ⓓ Chronological

8. **What organizational pattern does the author use in the conclusion paragraph? Write the correct answer in the box below.**

Ⓐ Problem and solution
Ⓑ Compare and contrast
Ⓒ Cause and effect
Ⓓ Chronological

9. **Which of the following is the author's intended audience?**

Ⓐ Teenage smartphone users
Ⓑ Teachers
Ⓒ Smartphone manufacturers
Ⓓ Parents of teenage smartphone users

10. **In Paragraph 2, what makes the quote by the teacher credible evidence?**

Name ______________________ Date ______________

Lesson 10 : Writing Routinely

1. Think of a movie you recently enjoyed. Write a one-paragraph review of the movie, focusing on what made it enjoyable.

2. Michael is writing an essay about his life-long hero. He chooses his Uncle Lance, who is a firefighter. What is the purpose of this writing? Write the correct answer in the box.

Ⓐ To inform
Ⓑ To persuade
Ⓒ To entertain
Ⓓ None of the above

3. Michael is writing an essay about his life-long hero. He chooses his Uncle Lance, who is a firefighter. What type of writing is this?

Ⓐ Informational
Ⓑ A narrative
Ⓒ An argument
Ⓓ A research project

4. Michael is writing an essay about the time his firefighter uncle rescued him from a burning house. What type of writing is this?

Ⓐ Informational
Ⓑ A narrative
Ⓒ An argument
Ⓓ A research project

5. "Think of someone you would consider to be your personal hero. Write an essay about a significant event in his or her life that caused you to choose this person as your hero."

Name ______________________ Date ______________

6. **Jada has been exploring the question, "How much of an impact does going to college in a student's hometown compare to going to college out of town?" She has gathered several credible sources of information and is now ready to compile her findings into an essay. What is the purpose of this writing?**

Ⓐ To inform
Ⓑ To persuade
Ⓒ To entertain
Ⓓ None of the above

7. **Jada has been exploring the question, "How much of an impact does going to college in a student's hometown compare to going to college out of town?" She has gathered several credible sources of information and is now ready to compile her findings into an essay. What type of writing is this?**

Ⓐ Informational
Ⓑ A narrative
Ⓒ An argument
Ⓓ A research project

8. **Think of a service project that would make a positive impact on your community. Write an argument to your classmates about why they should participate.**

9. **Think of an argument you've encountered recently that convinced you to do or believe something. Write a one paragraph summary of why the argument was convincing.**

10. **Jaqueline is writing a story about a little girl who dreams of growing up and becoming a fighter pilot. Through the course of the story, the little girl goes blind, shattering her dreams of becoming a pilot. What is the purpose of this writing?**

Ⓐ To inform
Ⓑ To persuade
Ⓒ To entertain
Ⓓ None of the above

Answer Key and Detailed Explanations

Chapter 2: Reading: Literature

Name ______________________ Date ______________

The Open Boat

Question No.	Answer	Detailed Explanations
1	B	*RL.9-10.1* The correct answer is B, because the feelings of mourning in the captain has almost made him cry. These show his feelings.
2	A	*RL.9-10.3* The correct answer is A because the four men know that they must work as a team to get through this ordeal.
3	C	*RL.9-10.2* The correct answer is C because each man is described and they work together under the command of the captain, so they worked as a team.
4	B	*RL.9-10.4* The correct answer is B because the situation is serious and a bucking bronco would show how violent the waves are pounding into the dinghy.
5	B	*RL.9-10.5* The correct answer is B because tension is created as the author explains each movement of the wave causing problems on the dinghy and the men unsure if they will make it to shore safely.
6	B	*RL.9-10.6* The correct answer is B because as a news reporter, he was not part of the ship's crew. He was like any other man on the ship.
7	D	*RL.9-10.7* The correct answer is D because the story shows how the men are struggling with the ocean and the letter compares the sea to a stage.

Name ______________________________ Date ________________

Two Thanksgiving Day Gentlemen

Question No.	Answer	Detailed Explanations
1	B	*RL.9-10.1* The correct answer is B because the word "annual" means that the two men go to the restaurant every year.
2	B	*RL.9-10.3* The correct answer is B because the waiters make a comment that shows they don't think the Old Gentleman should eat at the restaurant with Stuffy.
3	A	*RL.9-10.2* The correct answer is A because the two men ate a lot of dinner for Thanksgiving and it resulted in trips to the hospital.
4	C	*RL.9-10.4* The correct answer is C because the author is being funny when he describes Stuffy going to the hospital.
5	A	*RL.9-10.4* The correct answer is A because the men wanted to eat a lot and they stuffed themselves which is compared to them fighting against an enemy.
6	A	*RL.9-10.5* The correct answer is A because two separate stories exist after the dinner when Stuffy was taken to the hospital and the Old Gentleman being taken to the hospital.
7	D	*RL.9-10.5* The correct answer is D because a situation occurs that is not expected to happen.

Name ______________________ Date ______________

The McWilliamses and the Burglar Alarm

<table>
<tr><th>Question No.</th><th>Answer</th><th>Detailed Explanations</th></tr>
<tr><td>1</td><td></td><td>RL.9-10.1
The correct evidence would be "When we were finishing our house, we found we had a little cash left over on account of the plumber not knowing it," or "I was for enlarging the hearth with it because I was always unaccountably down on the hearth somehow."
These quotes from the passage reveal that Mr. McWilliam already has paid for another problem in the house and he doesn't want to pay for anything else. Also, he wants to pay for a hearth.</td></tr>
<tr><td>2</td><td></td><td>RL.9-10.3
Since Mr. McWilliams does not believe in burglar alarms, he almost expects burglars to come in. When the burglar does come in, Mr. McWilliams speaks with him in a humorous and respectful way due to Mr. McWilliams expecting the burglar to come in. Mr. McWilliams's expectations contribute to the theme because they are the same. They both expect the burglar alarms not to work and be invaluable. Therefore, when the burglar comes into the house, Mr. McWilliams is not surprised.</td></tr>
<tr><td>3</td><td></td><td>RL.9-10.3
<table>
<tr><th></th><th>calm and relaxed</th><th>greedy</th><th>closed-minded</th><th>fearful</th></tr>
<tr><td>Mr. McWilliams</td><td>○</td><td>○</td><td>●</td><td>○</td></tr>
<tr><td>Mrs. McWilliams</td><td>○</td><td>○</td><td>○</td><td>●</td></tr>
<tr><td>Burglar</td><td>●</td><td>○</td><td>○</td><td>○</td></tr>
<tr><td>Burlgar Alarm man</td><td>○</td><td>●</td><td>○</td><td>○</td></tr>
</table></td></tr>
<tr><td>4</td><td>B</td><td>RL.9-10.4
The correct answer is B because when the burglar took "a lot of miscellaneous property," he probably grabbed a bunch of things very fast without looking to see if they were valuable. The burglar did not go around and look carefully at what he would take.</td></tr>
<tr><td>5</td><td></td><td>RL.9-10.5
There are a few hints of foreshadow that the McWilliams will have trouble with burglars. First, Mr. McWilliams lets it be known at the beginning of the story that he does not see the value in the burglar alarms. Second, the burglar alarm man says that this burglar alarm only occurs on the first floor. When the burglar alarm man says that the alarm only works on the first floor, it is expected that another burglar will come until each floor contains the alarm.</td></tr>
</table>

Question No.	Answer	Detailed Explanations
6	D	*RL.9-10.6* The correct answer is D because in today's time, usually there are not coachmen because people don't ride horses for transportation purposes.
7		*RL.9-10.6* The narrator's point of view concerning the effectiveness of the burglar alarm can be described as worthless and costing too much money for how much he has to pay. This is because the husband shows signs that he really doesn't think that burglar alarms work and therefore are not worth the money.
8		*RL.9-10.7* The itemized list of materials used to secure the McWilliams' property shows that they had to ask the expert several times and either he didn't live close by or the parts he needed had to be shipped in. This is shown by having two sets of labor that Mr. McWilliam had to pay. Plus, there is a railroad charge, so the expert had to come from far away to secure their house.
9	A	*RL.9-10.7* The correct answer is A because the list is detailed so that the reader will sympathize that the McWilliamses are being taken advantage of with all of the costs.

Name ______________________ Date ______________

How an Old Man Lost his Wen

Question No.	Answer	Detailed Explanations
1		*RL.9-10.1* The old man didn't expect the demons to be there based on the following line from the passage "He at once thought that his friends had come to look for him." The old man expected his friends and thought that is what he heard, so he didn't expect to see demons instead.
2	D	*RL.9-10.1* The correct answer is D because he is upset with the lump in the other choices, but the audience is made aware that he will do something about it by the last line of the paragraph.
3		*RL.9-10.3* The old man only interacts as an observer because he watches what the demons do and is happy at what they are doing. Even though it seems that an observer can't be an interaction, but it is because the demons' behavior causes changes in the old man.
4		*RL.9-10.3* As the demons are having fun drinking wine and eating food, the man in the tree is acting happy and attentive while looking at the demons.The man continues to watch the demons to see what they are doing, and he does this because he is excited by what they are doing.
5		*RL.9-10.2* The man finds happiness after being depressed for so long and the two stories come together with the demons providing the old man with happiness. The old man tried to get the lump removed or do something about it, but he ended up finding happiness even though his lump was still on his face.
6	D	*RL.9-10.4* The correct answer is D because the lump is referred to later in the paragraph. This paragraph includes a synonym for the unknown word.
7	C	*RL.9-10.5* The correct answer is C because there are two stories included in this passage. The first story is about the old man upset with the lump on his skin. The second story involves the demons that the old man sees.
8		*RL.9-10.6* Based on the man's view of the demons, his point of view of the demons is that they are not threatening to him and are enjoying themselves. The demons are dancing and having fun which makes the old man enjoy watching them and he doesn't feel scared of them.

Name ____________________ Date ____________

Havells Stories from the Odyssey

Question No.	Answer	Detailed Explanations
1		*RL.9-10.1* Odysseus is concerned about the well-being of his crew by making sure his crew had enough food when it was stated "The first care of Odysseus was to supply the crews of his vessels, which were twelve in number, with fresh meat." This evidence supports the notion that Odysseus cared for his crew by giving them meat before leaving the boat and stepping foot on the land.
2	B	*RL.9-10.2* The correct answer is B because the Cyclops are described as being savages and that they should be feared.
3	B	*RL.9-10.7* The correct answer is B because both describe how the Cyclops lived off of the land by planting, which refers to their economy.
4		*RL.9-10.7* The structure of Havell's version of the Odyssey compares to the original version by Havell including more details whereas Homer's version gets straight to the point. The length of the original is much shorter due to it being a poem and Havell's version is longer because there are more explanations.
5		*RL.9-10.9*

	Havell's version	**Homer's original version**
____Created a sense of fear when Odysseus arrived	●	○
Portrays the Cyclops as a destructive force	○	●
Described the lack of government where the Cyclops lived	○	●

Question No.	Answer	Detailed Explanations
6	C	*RL.9-10.9* The correct answer is C because Homer's version describes that they made wine from the grape clusters.
7		*RL.9-10.9* The way that the Cyclops did not interact with those around them is shown in the original version by describing that they did not associate with their neighbors. In the original version, it shows that "each rules his race." This means that these creatures or people kept to themselves.
8		*RL.9-10.9* Havell wrote a description and narrative whereas Shakespeare's structure in his version is written as a rhyming poem. Having to rhyme certain words makes it more difficult to get the message across to the reader compared to Havell's way of describing what happened.

Name ______________________ Date ______________

Eleanor

<table>
<tr><th>Question No.</th><th>Answer</th><th>Detailed Explanations</th></tr>
<tr><td>1</td><td>A</td><td>RL.9-10.1
The correct answer is A because this shows that he became mad during this early time of his life.</td></tr>
<tr><td>2</td><td></td><td>RL.9-10.3
The answer is that Eleanor plays a part interacting in this passage by being an unseen or silent character because she does not interact with the characters. She is only described.</td></tr>
<tr><td>3</td><td>C</td><td>RL.9-10.2
The correct answer is C. The narrator admits that he is mad and deeply in love with Eleanor.</td></tr>
<tr><td>4</td><td>A</td><td>RL.9-10.5
The correct answer is A because the narrator relays information about his feelings before discussing the person he loves.</td></tr>
<tr><td>5</td><td></td><td>RL.9-10.4
<table>
<tr><th></th><th>to jut out</th><th>government land</th><th>strong emo-tion</th></tr>
<tr><td>"ardor of pas-sion"</td><td>○</td><td>○</td><td>●</td></tr>
<tr><td>"hung beetling around it"</td><td>●</td><td>○</td><td>○</td></tr>
<tr><td>"encircled do-main"</td><td>○</td><td>●</td><td>○</td></tr>
</table></td></tr>
<tr><td>6</td><td></td><td>RL.9-10.4
The narrator compares men who are in love with a woman to a vast ocean because they are both compassless.
This means that both of them do not follow a certain direction when they are in love with a woman because they almost go mad.</td></tr>
<tr><td>7</td><td>B</td><td>RL.9-10.6
The answer is B because the word "mad" was used in England during the 1700s and 1800s when many stories were written. Today, people do not use those words.</td></tr>
<tr><td>8</td><td></td><td>RL.9-10.6
The author believes that nature has many beautiful aspects to it just like the love of his life, Eleanor.
It seems that the explanation of Eleanor is written using an analogy of nature to show the author's love for her beauty.</td></tr>
</table>

Name ______________________________ Date ________________

Little Women

<table>
<tr><th>Question No.</th><th>Answer</th><th>Detailed Explanations</th></tr>
<tr><td>1</td><td></td><td>RL.9-10.1
The evidence from the passage that shows someone who was purposefully overlooked was when "Amy was asked, but Jo was not which was fortunate for all parties as her elbows were decidedly akimbo at this period of her life." This refers to Jo being left out of the fair because she did not have the behavior as Amy.</td></tr>
<tr><td>2</td><td>C</td><td>RL.9-10.3
The correct answer is C because Mrs. Chester wants Amy to decorate another table due to comments she made about her daughter. Mrs. Chester does not show anger but being serious about the situation.</td></tr>
<tr><td>3</td><td></td><td>RL.9-10.3
It was unusual for Mrs. Chester to ask Amy to go to another table because she is an adult and her daughter is jealous of Amy. An adult would not stoop to that level to get angry at someone who is their child's age especially when there is jealousy between the two.</td></tr>
<tr><td>4</td><td></td><td>RL.9-10.2
<table>
<tr><th></th><th>Mrs. Chester</th><th>May Chester</th><th>Amy</th></tr>
<tr><td>Refrain from making comments about people</td><td>○</td><td>○</td><td>●</td></tr>
<tr><td>Jealousy is a poor quality</td><td>○</td><td>●</td><td>○</td></tr>
<tr><td>Do not get involved in your daughter's problems.</td><td>●</td><td>○</td><td>○</td></tr>
</table></td></tr>
<tr><td>5</td><td></td><td>RL.9-10.4
The term was used to describe that any amount of women who get together would act this way. Since there is such a difference between the two numbers, it shows that any group of women would find it difficult to avoid skirmishes when they get together.</td></tr>
<tr><td>6</td><td></td><td>RL.9-10.4
Something that is merely a matter of expediency is something that is suitable to happen. That is why Mrs. Chester makes that statement because she wants Amy to work on a different table.</td></tr>
</table>

Question No.	Answer	Detailed Explanations
7	A	*RL.9-10.5* The correct answer is A because the characters and their feelings are described during different parts of the plot.
8		*RL.9-10.6* Amy is described in a positive light because first she is invited to the fair and she makes a joke about May. However, it is justified by the author's words. She also handles the situation with Mrs. Chester well. These things prove that Amy is viewed positively by the author with the way she conducted herself in these different situations.

Name ______________________ Date ____________

Muriels Bright Idea

<table>
<tr><th>Question No.</th><th>Answer</th><th>Detailed Explanations</th></tr>
<tr><td>1</td><td>D</td><td>RL.9-10.1
The correct answer is D. When the reader realizes that there are a bunch of different pockets, that shows that the apron is different.</td></tr>
<tr><td>2</td><td></td><td>RL.9-10.1
When the passage states “the original breadwinner has been long gone,” refers to the father having passed away.</td></tr>
<tr><td>3</td><td></td><td>RL.9-10.2
The apron is included as an important element of the theme because it represents her relationship to the members of her family.
The theme in the selection is about the importance of family and it is shown through Muriel’s apron.</td></tr>
<tr><td>4</td><td></td><td>RL.9-10.2
<table>
<tr><th></th><th>Muriel’s older siblings</th><th>Muriel</th><th>Narrator</th></tr>
<tr><td>sentimental about the apron</td><td>○</td><td>●</td><td>○</td></tr>
<tr><td>outsider from the family</td><td>○</td><td>○</td><td>●</td></tr>
<tr><td>workers who contribute to the family</td><td>●</td><td>○</td><td>○</td></tr>
</table></td></tr>
<tr><td>5</td><td>B</td><td>RL.9-10.2
The correct answer is B because Muriel is the youngest child in the family and she shows what she does to symbolize her love for her family.</td></tr>
<tr><td>6</td><td>A</td><td>RL.9-10.6
The correct answer is A because the narrator shows her impressiveness by the way she describes everything and how she interacts with Muriel.</td></tr>
</table>

Question No.	Answer	Detailed Explanations
7		*RL.9-10.5* The structure of the passage is organized so that the description of the family is included first in order to allow the reader to know that this family struggles. The reader needs some background information, but it gives a lot of information in order for the reader to fully understand the reason for Muriel's apron.
8		*RL.9-10.5* The story is paced so that there are descriptions of the family members, but it flows smoothly. The information is needed to be learned by the reader in order to completely understand why family is important.

Name ______________________________ Date ________________

John and Mary Lambs Version

Question No.	Answer	Detailed Explanations
1	A	*RL.9-10.3* The correct answer is A because Hermia would most likely become fearful that her father would resort to kill her for disobeying him.
2	B	*RL.9-10.4* The correct answer is B because it contains more formal old English words that were used and spoken in a more proper way during Shakespeare's time.
3	A	*RL.9-10.5* The correct answer is A because Shakespeare's version includes the dialogue or what the characters are saying to each other.
4	D	*RL.9-10.6* The correct answer is D because this culture reveals that women were not given the same rights as men due to their fathers being able kill their daughters for not marrying the men of their choice.
5	A	*RL.9-10.7* The correct answer is A because a large portion of this excerpt is given to the father, Egeus, to explain why he brought his daughter to court.
6	B	*RL.9-10.9* The correct answer is B because the Lamb's version describes Egeus as "stern" which makes him seem more like a human being and as a concerned father. In Shakespeare's version, he is described that he should be treated as a god.
7	B	*RL.9-10.9* The correct answer is B because the Lambs decided to explain the information about the law whereas Shakespeare relayed the information to the reader by the characters' words.

Name ______________________________ Date ______________

Sweetser's Ten Boys from Dickens

<table>
<tr><th>Question No.</th><th>Answer</th><th>Detailed Explanations</th></tr>
<tr><td>1</td><td>C</td><td>RL.9-10.6
The correct answer is C because in England they served pudding which is similar to a cake.</td></tr>
<tr><td>2</td><td></td><td>RL.9-10.7
Sweetser's version is different because she wrote more about the characters and Dickens' wrote a true story with a plot of events. Sweetser's version describes the characters and where the original story took place.</td></tr>
<tr><td>3</td><td></td><td>RL.9-10.7
<table>
<tr><th></th><th>Sweetser's version</th><th>Dickens' version</th><th>Both</th></tr>
<tr><td>a loving family</td><td>○</td><td>○</td><td>●</td></tr>
<tr><td>Tiny Tim as happy</td><td>●</td><td>○</td><td>○</td></tr>
<tr><td>that Tiny Tim might be mischievous</td><td>○</td><td>●</td><td>○</td></tr>
<tr><td>Tiny Tim as disabled</td><td>○</td><td>●</td><td>○</td></tr>
</table></td></tr>
<tr><td>4</td><td></td><td>RL.9-10.7
The correct answer is that the Dickens' version uses dialogue and descriptions about what the characters are doing to show the feelings and actions of the characters unlike Sweetser's version. The dialogue can be easily seen compared to Sweetser's version which summarizes the dialogue and actions that took place.</td></tr>
<tr><td>5</td><td></td><td>RL.9-10.7
The original version of the story uses more figurative language than Sweetser's by stating these examples of figurative language.</td></tr>
<tr><td>6</td><td></td><td>RL.9-10.9
Most likely, Sweetser found that this portion of the original passage focused on Tiny Tim because he was different than the other characters. The differences in stories make for memorable characters.</td></tr>
<tr><td>7</td><td></td><td>RL.9-10.9
The correct answer is that the Dickens' version uses dialogue and descriptions about what the characters are doing to show the feelings and actions of the characters unlike Sweetser's version. The dialogue can be easily seen compared to Sweetser's version which summarized in her own words the dialogue and actions that took place.</td></tr>
</table>

Question No.	Answer	Detailed Explanations
8	B	*RL.9-10.9* The correct answer is B because the first sentence of Sweetser's version criticizes that Dickens did not adequately explain what Tiny Tim looks like.
9		*RL.9-10.9* The correct answer is that Sweetser explains how much money Bob made per week working for Scrooge and how he had many children to take care of. It also explains that they did not have any luxuries. There are a few examples in the last paragraph of Sweetser's version which is not stated or emphasized as much regarding the amount of money the Cratchits made.

Answer Key and Detailed Explanations

Chapter 3
Reading: Informational Text

My Life and Work

Question No.	Answer	Detailed Explanations
1	B	RI.9-10.1 The correct answer is B because the Chicago packaging market used a similar process for packaging meat.
2	D	RI.9-10.1 The correct answer is D because if the process is used everywhere, then it would be very popular.
3	A	RI.9-10.2 The correct answer is A because this detail supports the central idea about the effectiveness of the assembly line. This shows how fast the process can go.
4		RI.9-10.3 The author does unfold the information about his assembly line by providing specific facts about each step of the process. Since the author used this process, he describes it in great detail.
5		RI.9-10.4 The usage of "had adopted the policy of 'man-high' work" refers to that the men would be on their toes concentrating about their work at all times. The reason for this is that the men could not take a break whenever they wanted to as that would cause the others in line to slow down and have to wait.
6		RI.9-10.4 (see table below)
7	C	RI.9-10.6 The correct answer is C because the author is proud that he can describe this new process for making cars.
8		RI.9-10.6 The author includes this detail because the next man on the assembly line would have to unscrew or undo what the previous man had done.

Question 6:

	a device for raising or lowering something	**electric generator**	**the framework on the car**
fly-wheel magneto	○	●	○
chassis	○	○	●
windlass	●	○	○

Name ______________________ Date ______________

How to Make a Bow and Arrow

Question No.	Answer	Detailed Explanations
1		

	"The strength of the Indian's bow and arrow is shown compared to that of others."	"Supplies are specific for optimum results."	"Techniques are described to keep the arrows strong."
After this the arrow should be painted, both to keep it from warping and to make it easier to find in the forest by its bright color.	○	○	●
We hear that many times Indians shot so hard that their arrows appeared on the far side of the animal.	●	○	○
These feathers are best made from either turkey or goose wings.	○	●	○

Question No.	Answer	Detailed Explanations
2	A	RI.9-10.3 The correct answer is A because the author explains the materials as the author is describing each part of the process.
3		RI.9-10.3 The bow and arrow are introduced in the passage by describing how powerful the Indian's bow and arrow was compared to others and the boys today should learn how to make and shoot them. This provides an introduction so that the reader will sense the importance of this bow and arrow as opposed to others.

4	D	RI.9-10.4 The correct answer is D because the midrib is described in the sentence as a vein which is close to the meaning of the stem.
5		RI.9-10.4 The ferrule is found on the top or bottom of an object.
6	B	RI.9-10.5 The correct answer is B because the author uses details to show step-by-step how to make the bow and arrow.
7		RI.9-10.6 The purpose of the drawing is to show how the different parts of the Indian's bow and arrow look like. This image allows the reader to see the different parts of the bow and arrow as well as the detailed steps to make them.
8		RI.9-10.7 There is a shaded part in the drawing for the bow because that allows the person to grip the bow before shooting the arrow. The student would need to infer that the shaded part would be drawn for a purpose and that would be where the person would be holding the bow.

Name ______________________________ Date ______________

How It Works

Question No.	Answer	Detailed Explanations
1	B	RI.9-10.1 The correct answer is B because this means that there are many other functions that could not be described.
2		RI.9-10.2 The central idea emerges through the description of the telegraph's parts and what it does to receive or transmit the message. Each part of the telegraph is explained along with how it functions in order to produce the entire message.
3		RI.9-10.2 The idea that is established by the author in the first paragraph is that with a few short steps a telegraph will function properly. The telegraph only seems to need a few parts and things to do before it will work according to the author.
4		RI.9-10.6 The purpose of the drawing is to show the reader where the wires are placed.
5	B	RI.9-10.4 The correct answer is B because a metropolis is a city like London.
6		RI.9-10.5 The author's claim about the importance of the telegraph developed through the way it works as well as the importance of the machine. This allows the author to reveal how important the telegraph is to the rest of the world as well as how simple it is to use.
7		RI.9-10.7 The drawing reveals one small part of the entire telegraph. It shows what the arm looks like and a description explains where the wires are and the way that the arm types the letters and symbols. The picture gives a visualization of one part to show how it works.
8		RI.9-10.7

	Drawing	Passage
the position of the wires in relation to the rest of the device	●	○
part of the device functions by electricity	○	●
as the message is received, it types it automatically	○	●

Name ____________________ Date ____________

Whales, Dolphins, and Porpoises of the Western North Atlantic

<table>
<tr><th>Question No.</th><th>Answer</th><th>Detailed Explanations</th></tr>
<tr><td>1</td><td>A</td><td>RI.9-10.1
The correct answer is A because this mentions the sperm whale and that it is a toothed whale unlike the other two.</td></tr>
<tr><td>2</td><td>C</td><td>RI.9-10.1
The correct answer is C because the only way to really determine the difference among these whales is by one feature and it is hard to see in the water.</td></tr>
<tr><td>3</td><td>D</td><td>RI.9-10.2
The correct answer is D because, in the first few paragraphs, the author explains how the dorsal fin is the body part that allows someone to distinguish the different species of whales.</td></tr>
<tr><td>4</td><td></td><td>RI.9-10.3
<table>
<tr><th></th><th>bumps on its head</th><th>has three ridges on its head</th><th>has a hump on its back with no dorsal fin</th></tr>
<tr><td>humpback</td><td>●</td><td>○</td><td>○</td></tr>
<tr><td>sperm</td><td>○</td><td>○</td><td>●</td></tr>
<tr><td>Bryde's whale</td><td>○</td><td>●</td><td>○</td></tr>
</table></td></tr>
<tr><td>5</td><td></td><td>RI.9-10.4
The author reveals the meaning of the word "rorquals" by identifying the same whale group with another name.The first time the rorquals are mentioned is when the author compares it to the same whale group but under a different name.</td></tr>
<tr><td>6</td><td>B</td><td>RI.9-10.4
The correct answer is B because the ridges are supportive of the main ridge. The word "supplemented" will help the reader figure out the meaning of the word.</td></tr>
<tr><td>7</td><td></td><td>RI.9-10.5
The author indirectly claims that different whales are difficult to tell apart. The author provides a lot of similarities among the whales and he explains how there are only certain body parts and its location to tell these animals apart.</td></tr>
<tr><td>8</td><td></td><td>RI.9-10.6
The author's purpose for writing this piece is to compare and contrast the different whales from the western North Atlantic Ocean.</td></tr>
</table>

John F. Kennedys Inaugural Address

Question No.	Answer	Detailed Explanations
1		RI.9-10.1 The evidence that suggests that Kennedy is referring to Alaska and Hawaii is when he states "To those new States whom we welcome to the ranks of the free." The newest states were Alaska and Hawaii and he is welcoming them to ranks of the free because they had just joined the Union.
2		RI.9-10.1 The evidence that supports Kennedy's decision to keep some laws and add others is when he states "signifying renewal, as well as change." This means that Kennedy will keep the laws that are working and change what needs to be changed.
3		RI.9-10.3 President Kennedy first speaks about the two different parts of the United States.
4	C	RI.9-10.4 The correct answer is C because the term "forebears" refers to the forefathers.

Textiles and Clothing

Question No.	Answer	Detailed Explanations
1	D	RI.9-10.1 The correct answer is D because it is an informative article including facts. It also discusses how to do spinning and weaving.
2		RI.9-10.1 The evidence that shows a gender bias regarding spinning and weaving is when the author states "in modern times transferred largely from man to machine were distinctively woman's employment." This shows that men were not considered to be part of the spinning or weaving jobs.
3	B	RI.9-10.2 The correct answer is B because the beginning of the passage is about the origin of spinning and weaving and then it goes into how to do the different types of spinning and weaving.
4		RI.9-10.3 The author introduces spinning and weaving to the reader by generally describing how to spin and weave using any supplies. The author describes how to spin and weave without bringing in specifics.
5	C	RI.9-10.4 The correct answer is C because the other examples have the same appearance as threads.
6		RI.9-10.5 The passage flows into a description of the types of spinning and weaving. It starts with a general statement about weaving and then describes where it was first used. The passage read easily since it followed the exact order of the events.
7		RI.9-10.6 The purpose of the author including the following line "The spindle is yet used by the North American Indians, the Italians, and in the Orient" is to show the different cultures that used spinning and weaving. Spinning and weaving is popular across many cultures.

Name ______________________ Date ______________

Common Sense

<table>
<tr><th>Question No.</th><th>Answer</th><th>Detailed Explanations</th></tr>
<tr><td>1</td><td></td><td>RI.9-10.2
<table>
<tr><th></th><th>Society</th><th>Government</th></tr>
<tr><td>Brings together what we like</td><td>●</td><td>○</td></tr>
<tr><td>Holds in our evil</td><td>○</td><td>●</td></tr>
<tr><td>Created by our desires</td><td>●</td><td>○</td></tr>
<tr><td>Produced by mischief</td><td>○</td><td>●</td></tr>
</table></td></tr>
<tr><td>2</td><td></td><td>RI.9-10.2
The theme that is addressed in "Common Sense" refers to the need for a new government due to the problems it is bringing onto the colonists. This theme can be shown in Paine's comparison of society and the government and the example he provides.</td></tr>
<tr><td>3</td><td></td><td>RI.9-10.3
In the third paragraph, the author includes an example to describe how the government would want to be built by the citizens themselves. Paine discusses how a group of people would function on an island in regard to creating a governmental system.</td></tr>
<tr><td>4</td><td></td><td>RI.9-10.3
Thomas Paine emphasizes that the government's purpose is to steal from the citizens in order to make sure the leaders are rich.
This is clearly shown in the first two paragraphs when it is comparing the government to society.</td></tr>
<tr><td>5</td><td>B</td><td>RI.9-10.5
The correct answer is B because Paine believes that the citizens should not be harmed and there is a difference between society and the government</td></tr>
<tr><td>6</td><td></td><td>RI.9-10.6
The purpose of Thomas Paine writing "Common Sense" was to cause the British government to change their laws or create a new government decided by the citizens in America.
Paine describes how a group of people should be able to make their decisions regarding their government.</td></tr>
</table>

Name ______________________ Date ______________

Declaration of Independence

<table>
<tr><th>Question No.</th><th>Answer</th><th>Detailed Explanations</th></tr>
<tr><td>1</td><td></td><td>RI.9-10.2
<table>
<tr><th></th><th>Disagreement of needed regulations</th><th>Did not use parts of Parliament bodies</th><th>Useless meetings</th></tr>
<tr><td>dissolved Representative Houses repeatedly</td><td>○</td><td>●</td><td>○</td></tr>
<tr><td>refused his Assent to Laws</td><td>●</td><td>○</td><td>○</td></tr>
<tr><td>called together legislative bodies at places unusual, uncomfortable, and distant</td><td>○</td><td>○</td><td>●</td></tr>
</table>
</td></tr>
<tr><td>2</td><td>A</td><td>RI.9-10.6
The correct answer is A because Jefferson's bitterness and anger is shown by his accusations of the British government.</td></tr>
<tr><td>3</td><td>B</td><td>RI.9-10.7
The correct answer is B due to its size and the significance is that this is when the United States had named itself.</td></tr>
<tr><td>4</td><td></td><td>RI.9-10.7
Comparing the published copy of the "Declaration of Independence" with the rough draft, Jefferson made many changes throughout. The changes can be seen on the rough draft by his strikethroughs.</td></tr>
<tr><td>5</td><td></td><td>RI.9-10.7
Most likely the most difficult section to write using the rough draft would be the beginning of the first and second paragraphs. This can be seen by the number of strikethroughs in these areas. Also, he scribbled out several sentences in these places so that they can't be read at all.</td></tr>
</table>

The Underground Railroad

Question No.	Answer	Detailed Explanations
1		RI.9-10.2 The central idea of the Craft's fear of the Fugitive Slave Law emerges when the definition is explained and how they could be sent back to Georgia. The Fugitive Slave Law is described after describing the Crafts' journey to freedom two years before.
2	D	RI.9-10.2 The correct answer is D because even though they earned their freedom for two years, they would always be fearful that a law would send them back to Georgia.
3		RI.9-10.3 The author wrote this passage in chronological order because it shows what the Crafts did prior to the Fugitive Slave Law. It shows how dangerous their journey was and that they were only safe for two years. This shows that the Fugitive Slave Law produced fear in former slaves who had escaped to the North.
4		RI.9-10.3 The Fugitive Slave Law allows former slave owners to reclaim their former slaves by having them sent back to their home state. The former slave owners could go and retrieve or offer rewards to people who turned in or provided information about the slave's location.
5	A	RI.9-10.5 The correct answer is A because the Fugitive Slave Law was shown as wrong after the Crafts made it to a free state.
6		RI.9-10.5 The second paragraph fits into the passage because it begins to describe where spinning and weaving came from. This allows the author's article to flow more smoothly into the more specific details explaining how to do specific spinning and weaving.
7	C	RI.9-10.6 The correct answer is C because the Fugitive Slave Law was revealed as a scary time for runaway slaves.

Name ______________________ Date ______________

The True Story of Our National Calamity of Flood, Fire and Tornado

Question No.	Answer	Detailed Explanations
1		RI.9-10.5 The author explains that legally the flooding was caused by an "act of God" because no one is to blame for this act. An "act of God" is more difficult to prepare for since these natural disasters cannot be predicted.
2		RI.9-10.5 The author claims that flooding seems to be the worst type of disaster. People often underestimate the devastation caused by flooding.
3		RI.9-10.5 The fifth paragraph shows how flooding is worse than earthquakes, explosions or wrecks by comparing these natural disasters.
4		RI.9-10.6 The author feels that flooding is awful. These lines from the passage shows what the author feels about flooding. Those who have never seen a great flood do not know the meaning of the Scriptural phrase, "the abomination of desolation." An explosion, a railroad wreck, even a fire—these are bad enough in their pictorial effect of shattered ruins and confusion. But for giving one an oppressive sense of death-like misery, there is nothing equal to a flood. I do not speak now of the loss of life, which is unspeakably dreadful, but of the scenic effect of the disaster. It just grips and benumbs you with its awfulness.
5	D	RI.9-10.7 The correct answer is D because this map shows where the "chief sufferers of the sweep of waters" was located on the map.
6		RI.9-10.7 The author is trying to prove by drawing the black dotted lines about the sweep of waters that the heavy waters affected many towns and cities. This means that many people were displaced or the towns were destroyed where many people lived.
7	A	RI.9-10.7 The correct answer is A because the harsh flooding is shown on the map and described in the passage.

Name ______________________ Date ______________

Question No.	Answer	Detailed Explanations
8		RI.9-10.7

	Important to the information in the passage	Not important to the information in the passage
location of rivers in comparison to the flooding	●	○
states' borders	○	●
location of Dayton, Ohio and its surrounding cities	●	○

Answer Key and Detailed Explanations

Chapter 4: Language Standards

Grammar and Usage Conventions

Question No.	Answer	Detailed Explanations
1	B	L.9-10.1 The answer is B because the phrase contains the verb of the sentence.
2	A	L.9-10.1 The answer is A because the phrase contains the noun and its modifiers.
3	C	L.9-10.1 The answer is C because the phrase begins with the preposition "in" and ends with "driveway" as the object of the preposition.
4	B	L.9-10.1 The answer is B because the sentence is composed of a dependent clause and does not communicate a complete thought.
5	C	L.9-10.1 The answer is C because the clause contains additional information about the noun "dog."
6	A	L.9-10.1 The answer is A because the sentence is composed of two independent clauses spliced together with a comma.
7	D	L.9-10.1 The answer is D because "buying" maintains the parallel structure established by "going."
8	A	L.9-10.1 The answer is A because the beginning phrase modifies the subject "Stacy."
9	B	L.9-10.1 The answer is B because it is a compound sentence that joins two independent clauses with a coordinating conjunction and requires a comma before the conjunction.
10	D	L.9-10.1 The answer is D because the "We went" in both independent clauses uses parallel structure.

Capitalization, Punctuation, and Spelling

Question No.	Answer	Detailed Explanations
1	C	L.9-10.2 The answer is C because only proper nouns are capitalized along with A and D.
2	B	L.9-10.2 The answer is B because the two independent clauses are closely related by the subject, so a semicolon is appropriate to join them, and the transition of "therefore" is also needed. A is a comma splice and C inaccurately uses a colon.
3		L.9-10.2 The sentence incorrectly uses the possessive "your" at the beginning when it should be the contraction of "you are," or "you're." The error is flipped later on in the sentence right before "contribution." The word should be "your" instead of "you're."
4	C	L.9-10.2 The answer is C because "weather" should be in place of "whether."
5	D	L.9-10.2 The answer is D because this is the definition of a comma splice.
6	B	L.9-10.2 The answer is B because a comma is not required after "homework."
7	D	L.9-10.2 The answer is D because it is the only sentence that uses the correct use of the homophone to/too/two both times it is used.
8		L.9-10.2 In the first sentence, president is a common noun not being used as a title for a specific president. In the second sentence, president is used as a proper noun as a title for Barack Obama, and should therefore be capitalized.
9	A	L.9-10.2 The answer is A because it misspells "acceptable" as "exceptable."

Question No.	Answer	Detailed Explanations
10		L.9-10.2 The answer is homophones because the given sentence is the definition for homophones.
11	D	L.9-10.2 The answer is D because a colon can be used to introduce a list of items in a series.
12		L.9-10.2 A homophone is a word that has the same sound as another word but its spelling and meanings are different Example to/ two/ too etc A word that is spelled like another word but it has a different sound and meaning is a homograph Example band - a ring, something that binds Band – a group Homonyms words which have the same sound or spelling but have different meaning. Example: Knew, New Synonyms are words which mean the same and Antonyms are opposites.

Functions of Language

Question No.	Answer	Detailed Explanations
1	C	L.9-10.3 The answer is C because The Atlantic is listed in the spot where the source title should appear in a Works Cited entry.
2	A	L.9-10.3 The answer is A because Julie Beck is listed in author position of the Works Cited entry.
3	B	L.9-10.3 The answer is B because fallible is synonymous with faulty just as credible is synonymous with trustworthy.
4	A	L.9-10.3 The answer is A because Shane Snow appears in the author position of the Works Cited entry.
5	B	L.9-10.3 The answer is B because Smartcuts appears in the book title position of the Works Cited entry.
6		L.9-10.3 Answers may vary, but answer should address the need to make writing have a varied rhythm created by a variety of sentence structures, which makes the writing more interesting for the reader.
7	C	L.9-10.3 The answer is C because MLA format is the standard format used for papers in an English class.
8	B	L.9-10.3 The answer is B because newspapers are written in AP style.
9	D	L.9-10.3 The answer is D because bibliography is synonymous with Works Cited.
10		L.9-10.3 Answers may vary, but answer should discuss how the Internet requires certain formatting and citation rules that didn't exist before the Internet age.

Determining Unknown Words

Question No.	Answer	Detailed Explanations
1	B	L.9-10.4 The answer is B because over means excessively, as in excessively confident, excessively burdened, and excessively joyed.
2	D	L.9-10.4 The answer is D because highlight is a synonym for accentuate.
3	B	L.9-10.4 The answer is B because anti- means against.
4	C	L.9-10.4 The answer is C because aud is the root word meaning sound.
5	D	L.9-10.4 The answer is D because the suffix -ism means belief.
6	A	L.9-10.4 The answer is A because graph is the root word meaning writing or printing.
7	C	L.9-10.4 The answer is C because the prefix dis- means not or a negation, as in disagree meaning not agreeing.
8	C	L.9-10.4 The answer is C because the root word gen means to birth.
9	B	L.9-10.4 The answer is B because a suffix is a letter or group of letters added to the end of a word to change its meaning.
10	A	L.9-10.4 The answer is A because despondent means without hope.

Name ______________________ Date ______________

Figurative Language

Question No.	Answer	Detailed Explanations
1		L.9-10.5 The answer is inexpensive because cheap has more negative associations with it than inexpensive.
2		L.9-10.5 The answer is shack because shack carries more of a connotation of a run-down building as opposed to home, which connotes comfort and family.
3	D	L.9-10.5 The answer is D because "old news," comprised of two contradictory terms, is an oxymoron.
4	B	L.9-10.5 The answer is B because the sentence is making a comparison between two unlike things, using the word like.
5	D	L.9-10.5 The answer is D because the sentence gives human characteristics to clouds, calling the rain tears.
6		L.9-10.5 The answer is casual because apathetic gives the connotation of complete disregard for something while casual connotes more easygoing playfulness.
7	A	L.9-10.5 The answer is A because the sentence makes a direct comparison between freedom and a sports car.
8	D	L.9-10.5 The answer is D because a song cannot literally play forever; it's an exaggeration.
9		L.9-10.5 The answer is "allusion" because an allusion is a reference to something in the past that would be easily recognizable to an audience.
10		L.9-10.5 A "denotation" is a dictionary definition of a word while a "connotation" is the meaning associated with a word.

Name ______________________ Date ______________

Academic and Domain-Specific Vocabulary

Question No.	Answer	Detailed Explanations
1	B	L.9-10.6 The answer is B because formidable means impressive in strength or excellence, which most fits the context.
2	C	L.9-10.6 The answer is C because flourish means to grow vigorously, which most fits the context.
3	A	L.9-10.6 The answer is A because jovial means full of or showing high-spirited merriment, which most fits the context.
4	D	L.9-10.6 The answer is D because unanimous means in complete agreement, which most fits the context.
5	A	L.9-10.6 The answer is A because voracious means desiring or craving food, which most fits the context.
6	C	L.9-10.6 The answer is C because a protagonist is the main character of a story.
7	D	L.9-10.6 The answer is D because analyze means to examine or think about something carefully, which most fits the context.
8	C	L.9-10.6 The answer is C because context means the parts of something written or spoken that immediately precede and follow a word or passage and clarify its meaning, which most fits the context.
9	B	L.9-10.6 The answer is B because estimate means to make an educated guess, which most fits the context.
10	D	L.9-10.6 The answer is D because assess means to make a judgment about someone or something after thinking carefully about it, which most fits the context.

Answer Key and Detailed Explanations

Chapter 5: Writing Standards

Name ____________________ Date ____________

Writing Arguments

<table>
<tr><th>Question No.</th><th>Answer</th><th>Detailed Explanations</th></tr>
<tr><td>1</td><td>C</td><td>W.9-10.1
Choice C is the best thesis statement because it clearly states a claim. It is both debatable and supported by evidence.</td></tr>
<tr><td>2</td><td>D</td><td>W.9-10.1
The answer is D because an argumentative thesis must be debatable and cannot just state a fact.</td></tr>
<tr><td>3</td><td>B</td><td>W.9-10.1
The answer is B because the counterclaim is when the opposing view is considered.</td></tr>
<tr><td>4</td><td>B</td><td>W.9-10.1
The answer is B. A conclusion should close with a call-to-action for the audience. This call-to-action should outline what you want the audience to do in response to your argument.</td></tr>
<tr><td>5</td><td>B</td><td>W.9-10.1
The answer is B because the other choices use informal language.</td></tr>
<tr><td>6</td><td>D</td><td>W.9-10.1
The answer is D because an argument should close with a call to action for the audience.</td></tr>
<tr><td>7</td><td>A</td><td>W.9-10.1
<table>
<tr><th></th><th>Credible Source</th><th>Non credible source</th></tr>
<tr><td>Wikipedia entry</td><td>○</td><td>●</td></tr>
<tr><td>A scientific journal article</td><td>●</td><td>○</td></tr>
<tr><td>A high school student's blog</td><td>○</td><td>●</td></tr>
<tr><td>A friend's opinion about a topic</td><td>○</td><td>●</td></tr>
</table>
</td></tr>
<tr><td>8</td><td>A</td><td>W.9-10.1
The answer is A because it makes a specific claim that the author will continue to support and debate throughout the rest of the argument.</td></tr>
<tr><td>9</td><td>D</td><td>W.9-10.1
The answer is D because A, B, and C are all valid sources of information.</td></tr>
<tr><td>10</td><td></td><td>W.9-10.1
Answers may vary. Because arguments are meant to persuade or convince the audience, knowing who the audience is and what is most likely to convince them is important so that you can tailor your writing toward that audience.</td></tr>
</table>

Informational Writing

Question No.	Answer	Detailed Explanations
1	B	W.9-10.2 The answer is B because A is narrative, C is an argument, and D is a poem.
2	C	W.9-10.2 The answer is C because the author presents an effect and uncovers the underlying cause of the effect.
3	A	W.9-10.2 The answer is A because the author presents a problem and then a clear solution to fix it.
4	D	W.9-10.2 The answer is D because the author gives the reader instructions on how to complete a task.
5	B	W.9-10.2 The answer is B because the author is comparing both the similarities between desktop and laptop computers and the differences.
6	A	W.9-10.2 The answer is A because the author wants to write about how to solve the problem of too much homework.
7	C	W.9-10.2 The answer is C because the second sentence is contrasting the information presented in the first sentence, which is communicated best by the transition, "however."
8	B	W.9-10.2 The answer is B because the author will be narrating a story of a past memory.
9	D	W.9-10.2 The answer is D because the author would be outlining steps in a specific order.

Name ______________________ Date ______________

Writing Narratives

<table>
<tr><th>Question No.</th><th>Answer</th><th>Detailed Explanations</th></tr>
<tr><td>1</td><td>B</td><td>W.9-10.3
The answer is B because the protagonist is the main character of the story.</td></tr>
<tr><td>2</td><td>D</td><td>W.9-10.3
The answer is D because the author uses third person pronouns and focuses only on the thoughts and emotions of one character.</td></tr>
<tr><td>3</td><td>A</td><td>W.9-10.3
The answer is A because this is the part of the plot diagram in which the setting and characters of a story are introduced.</td></tr>
<tr><td>4</td><td>C</td><td>W.9-10.3
The answer is C because a flashback takes the reader to a scene earlier in or before the story.</td></tr>
<tr><td>5</td><td>C</td><td>W.9-10.3
The answer is C because a static character remains the same throughout a story.</td></tr>
<tr><td>6</td><td></td><td>W.9-10.3
<table>
<tr><th></th><th>First Person</th><th>Second Person</th><th>Third Person</th></tr>
<tr><td>I, We</td><td>●</td><td>○</td><td>○</td></tr>
<tr><td>Me, Us</td><td>●</td><td>○</td><td>○</td></tr>
<tr><td>He, she, it</td><td>○</td><td>○</td><td>●</td></tr>
<tr><td>You, yours</td><td>○</td><td>●</td><td>○</td></tr>
</table>
</td></tr>
<tr><td>7</td><td>C</td><td>W.9-10.3
The answer is C because an internal struggle is a struggle the character has with himself/herself.</td></tr>
<tr><td>8</td><td>A</td><td>W.9-10.3
The answer is A because foreshadowing is the technique by which an author hints at something to occur later in the story.</td></tr>
<tr><td>9</td><td></td><td>W.9-10.3
Written answers will vary and should be assessed according to the standard Common Core writing rubric.</td></tr>
<tr><td>10</td><td>A</td><td>W.9-10.3
The answer is A because a dynamic character changes throughout the story.</td></tr>
</table>

Produce Clear and Coherent Writing

Question No.	Answer	Detailed Explanations
1	C	W.9-10.4 The answer is C because the author is providing information about bats.
2	A	W.9-10.4 The answer is A because the author uses the key word "should" and wants the reader to do something, using an argument for why they should.
3	C	W.9-10.4 The answer is C because A is missing a comma before "but" and uses "wood" instead of "would," B is missing an ending period, and D is missing the beginning capitalization and the comma before "but." C is written correctly.
4		W.9-10.4 The answer is True, because narrative is concerned with telling a story and mostly to entertain, as opposed to an argument.
5	D	W.9-10.4 The answer is D because A,B, and C should all be capitalized.
6	A	W.9-10.4 The answer is A because the author will be trying to convince the audience to make a decision.
7	C	W.9-10.4 The answer is C because Jennifer is writing a story or narrative about when she got her first pet.
8	D	W.9-10.4 The answer is D because the author intends to write a problem and possible solutions to that problem.
9	D	W.9-10.4 The answer is D because A uses "affect" instead of "effect," B uses "a" instead of "an," and C makes both of the mistakes of A and B while also missing the comma after "you." D is written correctly.
10	D	W.9-10.4 The answer is D because the author would be outlining steps in a specific order.

Develop and Strengthen Writing

Question No.	Answer	Detailed Explanations
1	A	W.9-10.5 The answer is A because it is the only sentence that has only one independent clause, though someone might be thrown off by the compound verb.
2	B	W.9-10.5 The answer is B because it is the only sentence with two independent clauses joined by a coordinating conjunction.
3	B	W.9-10.5 The answer is B because A has an introductory dependent clause, and so does C, though C is missing the required comma after an introductory clause or phrase. D is also missing the required comma even though it does begin with an introductory phrase.
4	C	W.9-10.5 The answer is C because editing is about correcting errors and C is about revising writing to make it better, not correcting a mistake.
5	C	W.9-10.5 The answer is C because revising is about improving writing, as in A, B, and D, but C is about correcting errors.
6	B	W.9-10.5 The answer is B because of the incorrect use of "your."
7	D	W.9-10.5 The answer is D because the other three options use weak linking and helping verbs. D uses a descriptive and active verb, "slithered."
8	D	W.9-10.5 The answer is D because the thesis statement should come just after the introduction in the first paragraph so that the reader is oriented into what the piece of writing is about.
9	A	W.9-10.5 The answer is A because the topic sentence establishes the topic and what will be said about the topic in a paragraph.
10	B	W.9-10.5 The answer is B because it misspells the word "kangaroo."

Name ______________________ Date ______________

Using Technology

Question No.	Answer	Detailed Explanations
1	D	W.9-10.6 The answer is D because it is the only choice that has a correctly formatted citation at the end of the sentence with the punctuation coming after the citation. The citation also includes the author's last name and the page number from which the quote was found.
2	A	W.9-10.6 The answer is A because MLA stands for Modern Language Association.
3	D	W.9-10.6 The answer is D because each of the programs is a valid word processing software to use.
4	C	W.9-10.6 The answer is C because paraphrasing is when you put someone else's words into your own words.
5		W.9-10.6 The answer is True, because any time you use information from a source, you must give credit to that source.
6		W.9-10.6 Citing sources shows the reader that you're giving credit to the sources you're using.
7	D	W.9-10.6 The answer is D because Lauren is claiming someone else's words as her own by not giving credit to her source.
8	C	W.9-10.6 The answer is C. A Works Cited page lists all the sources you used in your paper in alphabetical order by the author's last name.
9	C	W.9-10.6 The answer is C because MLA requires students to type their information with 12-point Times New Roman.
10	B	W.9-10.6 The answer is B because it's the cleanest and easiest way to indent a paragraph.

Conducting Research

Question No.	Answer	Detailed Explanations
1	D	W.9-10.7 The answer is D because the inquiry question helps you to narrow down your research so that you're not looking for any information about your subject, but specific information about the subject.
2	D	W.9-10.7 The answer is D because a works cited page citation requires A, B, and C.
3	D	W.9-10.7 The answer is D because A, B, and C would all require doing research in order to write.
4		W.9-10.7 The answer is True, because the question doesn't have you researching a specific environment.
5		W.9-10.7 A credible source will have a recognizable author. If the information is found online, more credible sources are found on websites that end with .edu or .gov. The date of publication is also important in order to help determine relevance of the information.
6	A	W.9-10.7 The answer is A because the author is describing a cause and its effect.
7	D	W.9-10.7 The answer is D because the author is offering possible solutions to a problem.
8	B	W.9-10.7 The answer is B because the question is more specific and narrows the scope of your research.
9	B	W.9-10.7 The answer is B because the answer to your inquiry question should be communicated in your research project through your thesis statement.
10		W.9-10.7 The answer is False, because research can't begin until after you've developed an inquiry question to guide your research so that you narrow what to look for.

Gathering Information

Question No.	Answer	Detailed Explanations
1	B	W.9-10.8 The answer is B because an autobiography is a first-hand account of someone's life.
2	D	W.9-10.8 The answer is D because A, B, and C are all first-hand accounts while a biography is a secondary account.
3		W.9-10.8 Primary sources are first-hand accounts of information or events while secondary sources are second-hand accounts.
4	A	W.9-10.8 The answer is A because in-text citations are a way for the author to properly give credit to a source whose information the author used.
5		W.9-10.8 Answers may vary. An important reason to gather information from multiple sources is to help eliminate any potential bias in the author. An author with an open mind and a willingness to look at different perspectives is often able to find insights that biased authors will typically be blind to.
6	B	W.9-10.8 The answer is B because free internet search engines, such as Google and Bing, can't be trusted to direct you to the most authoritative sources.
7		W.9-10.8 The answer is False, because a diary is a first-hand account and not from a secondary person presenting the information.
8	C	W.9-10.8 The answer is C because the author wants to discuss the effects of Obama's presidency, which is the cause.
9	C	W.9-10.8 The answer is C because it is the only source that comes directly from Steinbeck himself.
10		W.9-10.8 Answers vary. Since the teacher also taught Melanie's sister, it's likely that the teacher had already read the essay submitted by Melanie that was really written by her sister. Melanie's teacher will likely accuse Melanie of plagiarizing her sister's work.

Name ______________________ Date ______________

Using Textual Evidence

Question No.	Answer	Detailed Explanations
1	B	W.9-10.9 The answer is B because the author is cautioning the audience against allowing teenagers to overuse smartphones.
2		W.9-10.9 Answers will vary. Sample: Though smartphones are widely used and provide a number of conveniences, teenagers especially are showing signs of overuse of the technology. Students are being distracted both at school and at home by their smartphones. Parents should talk to their kids about responsible smartphone use.
3	D	W.9-10.9 The answer is D because the author's focus throughout the passage is how smartphones are distracting even though they are also useful.
4	D	W.9-10.9 The answer is D because Paragraph 4 considers the opposition to the author's view.
5		W.9-10.9 The author uses research from studies on sleep deprivation due to smartphone use and other anecdotal evidence of smartphones distracting teenagers from their education and home lives.
6	D	W.9-10.9 The answer is D because the author is encouraging parents to have a conversation with their kids about the dangers of overusing smartphones.
7	C	W.9-10.9 The answer is C because in Paragraphs 2 and 3, the author describes the negative effects of smartphone overuse.
8	A	W.9-10.9 The answer is A because the author reiterates the problem he's been describing since the first paragraph and now offers a possible solution to the problem.
9	D	W.9-10.9 The answer is D because the call to action in the conclusion paragraph addresses parents and what they should do.
10		W.9-10.9 The teacher is a first-hand observer of the problems the author is describing as a result of smartphones. She can be believed because she's describing what she's personally seen and how it affects her teaching.

Name ______________________ Date ______________

Writing Routinely

Question No.	Answer	Detailed Explanations
1		W.9-10.10 Written answers will vary and should be assessed according to the standard Common Core writing rubric.
2	A	W.9-10.10 The answer is A because Michael will be informing the reader about his uncle.
3	A	W.9-10.10 The answer is A because the essay is about his uncle and won't be focusing on one particular story about his uncle, but will likely include several short narratives as supporting evidence for the information presented in the essay.
4	B	W.9-10.10 The answer is B because the author will be focusing on a story about his uncle.
5		W.9-10.10 Written answers will vary and should be assessed according to the standard Common Core writing rubric.
6	A	W.9-10.10 The answer is A because Jada will be presenting the information she's gathered in a coherent report of her findings to her audience.
7	D	W.9-10.10 The answer is D because the author is researching information based on a focused inquiry question.
8		W.9-10.10 Written answers will vary and should be assessed according to the standard Common Core writing rubric.
9	B	W.9-10.10 Written answers will vary and should be assessed according to the standard Common Core writing rubric.
10	C	W.9-10.10 The answer is C because the author is writing a fictional story to entertain an audience.

Additional Information

High School ELA 1 FAQs

What will ELA 1 Assessment Look Like?

In many ways, the ELA 1 assessments will be unlike anything many students have ever seen. The tests require students to complete tasks to assess a deeper understanding of the CCSS in domains such as Reading Literature, Reading Informational Text, Language, Writing sections.

What are the English Language Arts credit programs offered in High Schools?

Most of the High Schools offer ELA 1, ELA 2, ELA 3 programs.

What item types are included in the Online ELA 1 Test?

Because the assessment is online, the test will consist of a combination of new types of questions:

1. Drag and Drop
2. Drop Down
3. Essay Response
4. Extended Constructed Response
5. Hot Text Select and Drag
6. Hot Text Selective Highlight
7. Matching Table In-line
8. Matching Table Single Response
9. Multiple Choice – Single Correct Response, radial buttons
10. Multiple Choice – Multiple Response, check boxes
11. Numeric Response
12. Short Text
13. Table Fill-in

Discover Engaging and Relevant Learning Resources

Lumos EdSearch is a safe search engine specifically designed for teachers and students. Using EdSearch, you can easily find thousands of standards-aligned learning resources such as questions, videos, lessons, worksheets and apps. Teachers can use EdSearch to create custom resource kits to perfectly match their lesson objective and assign them to one or more students in their classroom.

To access the EdSearch tool, use the search box after you log into Lumos StepUp or use the link provided below.

www.lumoslearning.com/a/edsearchb	

The Lumos Standards Coherence map provides information about previous level, next level and related standards. It helps educators and students visually explore learning standards. It's an effective tool to help students progress through the learning objectives. Teachers can use this tool to develop their own pacing charts and lesson plans. Educators can also use the coherence map to get deep insights into why a student is struggling in a specific learning objective.

Teachers can access the Coherence maps after logging into the StepUp Teacher Portal or use the link provided below.

www.lumoslearning.com/a/coherence-map	

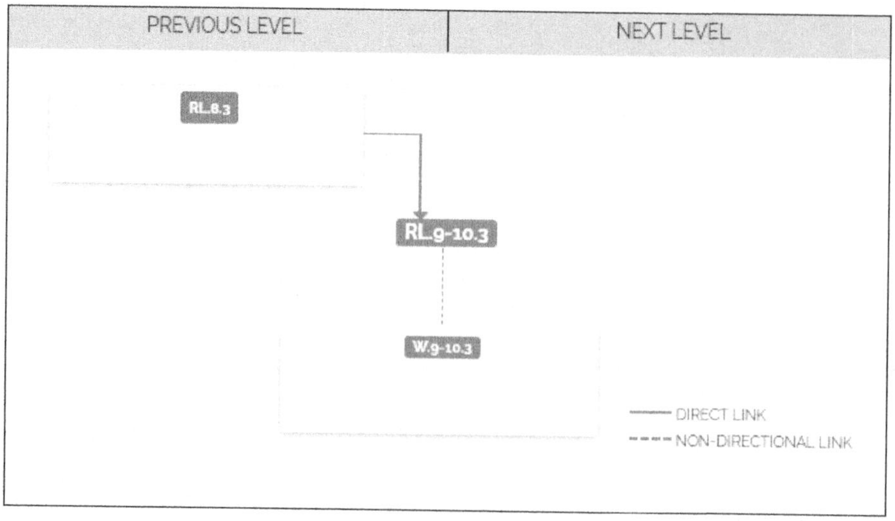

Progress Chart

Passage/ Lesson	Lesson/Passage Name	Q No.	Page No.	Practice		Mastered	Re-practice /Reteach
				Date	Score		
Chapter 2	**Reading: Literature**		**8**				
Passage 1	The Open Boat	1	8				
		2					
		3					
		4					
		5					
		6					
		7					
Passage 2	Two Thanksgiving Day Gentle-men	1	12				
		2					
		3					
		4					
		5					
		6					
		7					
Passage 3	The McWilliamses and the Bur-glar Alarm	1	15				
		2					
		3					
		4					
		5					
		6					
		7					
		8					
		9					
Passage 4	How an Old Man Lost his Wen	1	20				
		2					
		3					
		4					
		5					

Standard	Lesson	Q No.	Page No.	Practice		Mastered	Re-practice /Reteach
				Date	Score		
		6					
		7					
		8					
Passage 5	Havells Stories from the Odyssey	1	24				
		2					
		3					
		4					
		5					
		6					
		7					
		8					
Passage 6	Eleanor	1	28				
		2					
		3					
		4					
		5					
		6					
		7					
		8					
Passage 7	Little Women	1	31				
		2					
		3					
		4					
		5					
		6					
		7					
		8					
Passage 8	Muriels Bright Idea	1	35				
		2					
		3					
		4					

Standard	Lesson	Q No.	Page No.	Practice		Mastered	Re-practice /Reteach
				Date	Score		
		5					
		6					
		7					
		8					
Passage 9	John and Mary Lambs' Version	1	39				
		2					
		3					
		4					
		5					
		6					
		7					
Passage 10	Sweetser's Ten Boys from Dick-ens	1	43				
		2					
		3					
		4					
		5					
		6					
		7					
		8					
		9					
Chapter 3	**Reading: Informational Text**		47				
Passage 1	My Life and Work	1	47				
		2					
		3					
		4					
		5					
		6					
		7					
		8					

Standard	Lesson	Q No.	Page No.	Practice		Mastered	Re-practice /Reteach
				Date	Score		
Passage 2	How to Make a Bow and Arrow	1	50				
		2					
		3					
		4					
		5					
		6					
		7					
		8					
Passage 3	How It Works	1	54				
		2					
		3					
		4					
		5					
		6					
		7					
		8					
Passage 4	Whales, Dolphins, and Porpoises of the Western North Atlantic	1	58				
		2					
		3					
		4					
		5					
		6					
		7					
		8					
Passage 5	John F. Kennedys Inaugural Address	1	62				
		2					
		3					
		4					
Passage 6	Textiles and Clothing	1	65				
		2					
		3					

Standard	Lesson	Q No.	Page No.	Practice		Mastered	Re-practice /Reteach
				Date	Score		
		4					
		5					
		6					
		7					
Passage 7	Common Sense	1	68				
		2					
		3					
		4					
		5					
		6					
Passage 8	Declaration of Independence	1	71				
		2					
		3					
		4					
		5					
Passage 9	The Underground Railroad	1	74				
		2					
		3					
		4					
		5					
		6					
		7					
Passage 10	The True Story of Our National Calamity of Flood, Fire and Tornado	1	78				
		2					
		3					
		4					
		5					
		6					
		7					
		8					

Standard	Lesson	Q No.	Page No.	Practice		Mastered	Re-practice /Reteach
				Date	Score		
Chapter 4	**Language**		**82**				
Lesson 1	Grammar and Usage Conventions	1	82				
		2					
		3					
		4					
		5					
		6					
		7					
		8					
		9					
		10					
Lesson 2	Capitalization, Punctuation, and Spelling	1	85				
		2					
		3					
		4					
		5					
		6					
		7					
		8					
		9					
		10					
		11					
		12					
Lesson 3	Functions of Language	1	88				
		2					
		3					
		4					
		5					
		6					
		7					
		8					
		9					
		10					

Standard	Lesson	Q No.	Page No.	Practice		Mastered	Re-practice /Reteach
				Date	Score		
Lesson 4	Determining Unknown Words	1	90				
		2					
		3					
		4					
		5					
		6					
		7					
		8					
		9					
		10					
Lesson 5	Figurative Language	1	92				
		2					
		3					
		4					
		5					
		6					
		7					
		8					
		9					
		10					
Lesson 6	Academic and Domain-Specific Vocabulary	1	94				
		2					
		3					
		4					
		5					
		6					
		7					
		8					
		9					
		10					

Standard	Lesson	Q No.	Page No.	Practice		Mastered	Re-practice /Reteach
				Date	Score		
Chapter 4	**Writing Standards**		**97**				
Lesson 1	Writing Arguments	1	97				
		2					
		3					
		4					
		5					
		6					
		7					
		8					
		9					
		10					
Lesson 2	Informational Writing	1	100				
		2					
		3					
		4					
		5					
		6					
		7					
		8					
		9					
Lesson 3	Writing Narratives	1	102				
		2					
		3					
		4					
		5					
		6					
		7					
		8					
		9					
		10					

Standard	Lesson	Q No.	Page No.	Practice		Mastered	Re-practice /Reteach
				Date	Score		
Lesson 4	Produce Clear and Coherent Writing	1	104				
		2					
		3					
		4					
		5					
		6					
		7					
		8					
		9					
		10					
Lesson 5	Develop and Strengthen Writing	1	106				
		2					
		3					
		4					
		5					
		6					
		7					
		8					
		9					
		10					
Lesson 6	Using Technology	1	108				
		2					
		3					
		4					
		5					
		6					
		7					
		8					
		9					
		10					

Standard	Lesson	Q No.	Page No.	Practice		Mastered	Re-practice /Reteach
				Date	Score		
Lesson 7	Conducting Research	1	110				
		2					
		3					
		4					
		5					
		6					
		7					
		8					
		9					
		10					
Lesson 8	Gathering Information	1	112				
		2					
		3					
		4					
		5					
		6					
		7					
		8					
		9					
		10					
Lesson 9	Using Textual Evidence	1	114				
		2					
		3					
		4					
		5					
		6					
		7					
		8					
		9					
		10					

Standard	Lesson	Q No.	Page No.	Practice		Mastered	Re-practice /Reteach
				Date	Score		
Lesson 10	Writing Routinely	1	117				
		2					
		3					
		4					
		5					
		6					
		7					
		8					
		9					
		10					

Made in the USA
Middletown, DE
25 January 2023

23107342R00104